THE ART OF
Wheelbuilding

A BENCH REFERENCE FOR
NEOPHYTES, PROS AND WHEELAHOLICS

Gerd Schraner

BUONPANE PUBLICATIONS

Dedicated

to my wife Jackie
for always understanding,

to the DT Swiss family
for always helping and

to Wolfgang Renner
for always supporting.

Acknowledgments

It is impossible to write a book such as this without the assistance and support from many quarters.

Valuable assistance came from:

Natali Arn (drawings), Vincenne Buonpane (publishing), Clean Slate (design), Sue Buri (logistics), Dane Kurth (translation) and Marco Zingg (support).

In addition to their time-consuming jobs, they all spent time in order to help me to realize this project. I take this opportunity of thanking them.

Numerous other people also helped indirectly to make this possible. Representing them all I would like to thank:

Paul Aieta	Tim Breen	Fritz Brühlmann
Arnold Gerber	Daniel Gisiger	Patrick Moerlen
Christian Müller	Wolfgang Renner	Richard Wade

Contents

Introduction

I'm one of the lucky ones, because my life has been enriched by my work with wheels.

I've been blessed with the ability to build wheels which "stand." The end users value and respect my work. And it has even helped to form life-long friendships.

I'm constantly fascinated by my work. I never cease to learn, to experience something new, to take the opportunity of studying and evaluating new products which appear on the component market.

I'm practically addicted to my job, because every one of my handbuilt wheels radiates a certain something which is impossible to describe. A respected journalist once put it succinctly:

"Wheelbuilding has a philosophical, even a sensual dimension to it."

Many people call me a "wheel guru," which honors and flatters me. But a guru is an all-knowing teacher, which I neither am nor wish to be. Many paths lead to success and everyone has his own method of walking that path. This book describes my method and it is up to the reader to pick out the parts which are most useful to him or her and to ignore the rest.

Only a few of the methods and tricks described in this book are "all my own work." Many of them were picked up from colleagues, tried out and — if they passed my personal tests — I adopted them for myself.

My many years as a race mechanic for both amateur and professional racers on road and track helped me to put old and new methods and ideas concerning truing to the test under the toughest conditions imaginable.

Thanks to the friendly way in which I was accepted by the bike scene, and the constant encouragement, I finally took it upon myself to write this book. In the following pages I will try to describe, step by step, how to build a high quality wheel and take the mystery out of the selection of suitable components.

I am neither engineer nor author, just a simple artisan. In these, the autumn years of my life, it is my aim to publish all my wheelbuilding secrets for everyone who is interested, be they beginners or professionals, in as simple a manner as possible. I have deliberately omitted high-tech jargon, complicated formulae and incomprehensible graphics. I sincerely hope it will also be of interest to bike enthusiasts who do not build their own wheels, and to those who just wish for technical information to help them understand and enjoy their bikes even more.

In these days of digitalization and CNC production the old proverb "The work commends the workman" is more true than ever.

The artisan who takes pleasure in building beautiful, precise wheels will probably never become rich, but his life will be enriched!

And if this book inspires some of its readers to learn the wheelbuilding trade or even simply to put in a little more practice, then the work I have put into its pages has been rewarded.

— *Gerd Schraner*

The spoked wheel

PART 1

The spoked wheel

Classic, Perfection, Fascination

Classic

Time stands still for the classic wheel. Despite the appearance on the market of disk wheels, three and four spoke carbon wheels in all their variations, the classical spoked wheel is simply irreplaceable.

It is classical because it has proved itself since the bicycle was invented, because it is the cheapest variety and because riders simply never tire of their comfort and variability (types and number of spokes, lacing patterns).

Watching today's cycle racing scene, one tends to notice that all carbon wheels are slowly disappearing, or are at least being replaced by one of their components, carbon fiber rims.

Perfection

Spoked wheels, comprising of the best components available and time-consumingly built by professionals, are handworkers' masterpieces of the highest order.

They give the owner not only the satisfaction and knowledge of owning the best, but also the confidence of carefree riding.

Fascination

A professionally built spoked wheel is like a jewel. When the wheel turns, the quality components glitter like gold and silver. The gentle hum from the spokes, the feeling on straights, in corners, uphill and the immediate reaction when accelerating can be compared to nothing else in the world.

At Six Day Races, where racing bikes hurtle around the oval track, or at the Tour de France, when a field of 180 stream out of the sun's haze towards you, the glitter and the sound of the tires is simply breathtaking.

And those who feel this fascination to the very depths of their souls — they are the Wheelaholics!

Handbuilt wheels

Manual wheelbuilding is one of the remaining skilled crafts in bicycle manufacturing.

This is the stage at which wheelbuilders can prove their craftsmanship and whether they have a true relationship with their work.

Almost anyone can build a good wheel. You need neither a high school education nor be computer-literate, but simply a lot of practice. You can even make a mistake - but you should make it only once. Beginners need patience, but they shouldn't lose confidence if something goes wrong. Care, patience and self-criticism are the most valuable characteristics of a professional wheelbuilder.

The rewards are satisfied users, be they active racing cyclists, bikers or anyone else who gets around on two wheels!

Wheelbuilding brings its own reputation. If you are a master of your craft, word will get around and you'll soon make a name for yourself!

Almost everything on a modern bicycle is at an even, high technical standard - the exception are the wheels which sometimes are still the cause of small headaches.

For road and mountain bike use, high-end components, including hubs, rims and spokes, are mechanically perfect and highly reliable, but, let us never forget the important fact that they are meant primarily for racers and bikers weighing a maximum of 188 lbs. (85 kg).

Heavier riders put a lot more strain on their wheels and, as a result, will tend to have problems with mechanically-built wheels - problems which will result in time-consuming, costly adjustments and repair in a bike workshop. This is where the good wheelbuilder comes into his own, being more in a position to fulfill a rider's specific wishes and requirements (type of usage, rider's weight, etc.).

During a dialogue with the rider one can offer one's opinion about a rider's most unusual and seemingly absurd demands and suggest other possibilities. But a wheelbuilder should never violate the basic principles of wheelbuilding, nor ignore the inner warning voice of experience simply to please a customer. Sooner or later, the price will be paid.

The wheelbuilder should be absolutely satisfied with his work - the final product, his wheel, must "stand." In other words, once it leaves his workshop, it should never need re-truing and it will never break a spoke. He should be confident enough to guarantee the wheel for the rim's lifetime.

Handbuilt wheels have their own character. I can tell the work of many of my own colleagues apart - and all of them are professionals.

Top-class wheelbuilders can even look at a series of ten of their own wheels, built using identical components, and say which they feel is the best.

1997 Tour de France, the last miles.

Their products leave the workshop with pride and a little sadness, rather like chicks who have grown up and are now leaving the nest.

Some work well done.

Machine-built wheels

The majority of all spoked wheels available today are machine-built and, despite huge differences in price categories, practically all spoked wheels installed on complete bikes built in factories (OEM) are machine-built.

Over-the-counter wheels sold to dealers (ASM) as single units or in pairs, and whose components reflect the current market demands, are mostly machine-built. For wheels with identical components, the price is calculated on the actual machining time.

Wheeltruing Roboter (HOLLAND MECHANICS)

Complete wheels built by leading manufacturers such as CAMPAGNOLO (Shamal, Vento, Zonda), MAVIC (Helium, Cosmic, Crossmax) or TREK (Rolf), can be found in both handbuilt and machine-built wheel categories. All these expensive models (fewer spokes and high-end components) are built by hand.

Qualitative comparisons of handbuilt vs machine-built wheels

Both types of products result in qualities ranging from good to poor.

Manual wheelbuilding by professionals always results in the best quality. An artisan can apply his knowledge, experience and love for his work. An example is the installation of washers beneath the spoke head, which can greatly extend the wheel's life. A machine simply cannot do that (yet). Aligning spokes in a direct line, another manual step, is difficult work for a machine, while multiple flexing during the truing stage requires yet more expensive machine time. The quality of the machine-built wheel is therefore dependent on the number of cycles and steps of which the machine is capable.

The quality of the majority of machine-built wheels from the Far East is in some cases embarrassingly poor - dealers could write a book about the stories they have to tell. Frustration and market demands have therefore caused an increasing return of the production of high-quality wheels to Europe and the U.S.A. Several companies, for example Colorado Cyclist in Colorado, Quality Bicycle Products in Minnesota, and Service Cycle in New York, combine hand-building experience with high-end components to produce machine-built wheels of a high standard, which are often of a better quality than average handbuilt wheels.

At a bike show, I once had the opportunity to compare a wheel I had built myself with one produced at the show by the leading manufacturer, HOLLAND MECHANICS. The quality of the machine-built wheel, though requiring a number of production stages, left little to be desired. After the wheel had been run-in, however, it did need some minor retruing.

Layout of a central controlled truing facility. (HOLLAND MECHANICS)

Some handmade wheels, made with the best intentions but by people lacking professional knowledge, can cause a lot of heartache. People unsure of themselves in this field and who have neither the time nor the interest to learn are therefore advised to purchase good quality ready-made wheels.

Finally, I would like to note that the perfect, hand-built wheel is the most expensive of all, due to the work required - about one hour of high-precision, manual labor. The final decision between buying "handmade" or ready-made wheels therefore lies solely with the user. Should he decide on the former, then the value of his or her bike will be enhanced by these worry and problem-free "jewels."

Eddy Merckx - The role model

As an artisan with a great respect for ethics, my goal has always been perfection and absolute professionalism. I had several role models, of which Eddy Merckx influenced me the most. I didn't know him personally during his active career, but by observing his professionalism I was able to learn a great deal and I attempted to copy his excellent trait.

Before working as a mechanic at 6-Day Races myself, I had the opportunity, as a spectator at the 1977 Zürich 6-Day Race, to sit near Eddy's "bunk", where he was attended to by his helpers and where I could closely observe the way his mechanics looked after his material. As the star of the show and highest earner of the race, Eddy did his job with exemplary concentration, few words and great professionalism.

After a rest period, he was on his bike and in position well before time, while the race director had to plead with his colleagues to get onto the track if they wanted to earn some money. In Eddy's "bunk", clean shorts, shirts, socks and gloves were neatly piled and ready to be worn. And he used them. Unlike some of his colleagues, he never wore sweaty or dirty racing gear and - in contrast to many colleagues, you never saw him in worn-out stretched or malformed racing shorts, which were still made of wool in those days.

His track wheels - five pairs for each 6-Day Race, were technically the best that money could buy and were perfectly maintained by his personal mechanic. Race wheel rims didn't have anodized

Eddy Merckx

surfaces in those days, but the pure aluminum of his rims was highly polished, so highly that it looked like chrome. Even the sides of the delicate tubulars (165 grams) were, when necessary, rubbed down and renewed using a rubber solution. The traditional white handlebar tape was changed every day.

Eddy even tried to suit his riding position to the characteristics of the track. During rest periods he took the time to work on his position with his mechanic, reaching his ideal position step by step. I don't know anything about racing, but I do know something about racing material. After all my observation of Eddy Merckx, I think I can say that his professionalism in the matter of details, transposed into more important matters such as team management, training and racing, and made him into the greatest racing cyclist of all time.

PART 2

Wheel components

Spokes

Nipples

Hubs

Rims

Wheel components

Spokes

There are many different types of spokes on offer by both manufacturers and shops, but only some of them are taken into consideration by the wheelbuilder for the production of high-quality wheels.

Types of Spokes

Straight gauge, double-butted, triple-butted and bladed are the four types of spokes preferred by professional wheelbuilders. (Diagram on the opposite page.) They are also produced without elbows (e.g. PULSTAR, CAMPAGNOLO-Shamal and CAMPAGNOLO-Vento).

Other types of spokes, for example wavy or the headless type of zig-zag spokes, are not too popular despite the apparent advantages with which they are credited. The former cannot be permanently tensioned and one misses the hub/spoke seating of the latter. This type of spoke, when highly pre-tensioned and especially when used on the right side of the rear wheel, tends to work its way out of the hub flange.

Straight Gauge Spokes

Characteristics

Same diameter (ØA), 2.0 or 1.8 mm from the spoke head to the end of the thread.

Applications

A robust, all-round spoke. Advantage: Inexpensive because of the low number of manufacturing stages necessary. Disadvantage: the rigid, practically non-damping arm, which, when overloaded, transfers all loads to the elbow. Is not particularly recommended for high quality wheels, because the savings on the spoke costs are not in relation to the amount of work involved.

Bladed or aero-spokes

Characteristics

Straight spoke, whose central area is worked flat to a thickness of 1.0 mm. Same diameter (ØA), usually 2.0 mm, at the spoke elbow and the thread. Good cw (aerodynamics) coefficient and

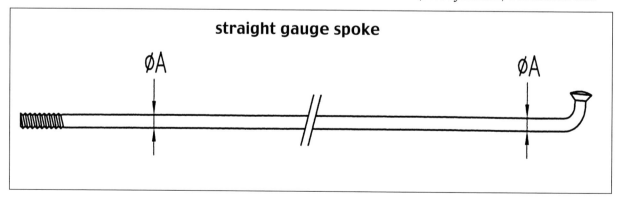

straight gauge spoke

ØA   ØA

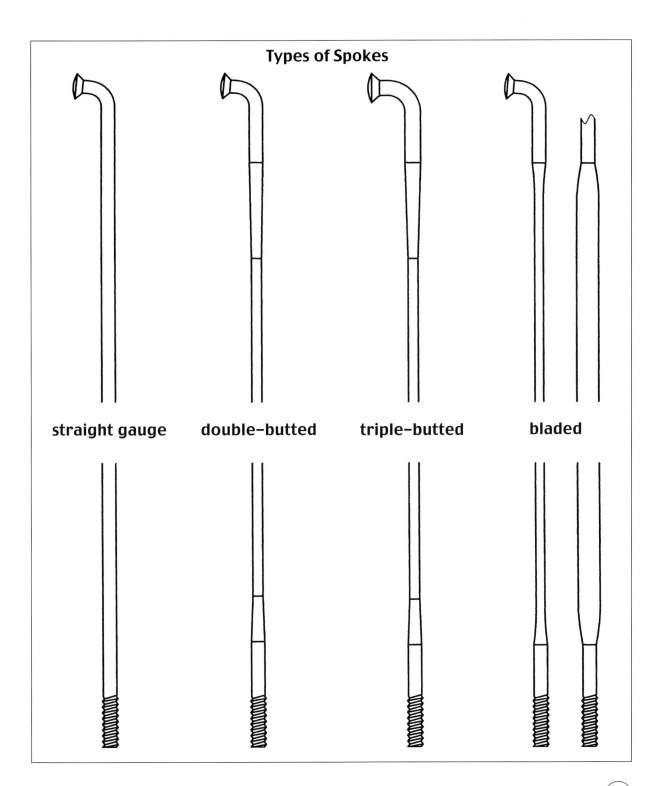

Types of Spokes

straight gauge   **double-butted**   **triple-butted**   **bladed**

high loadability. They look fascinating and tend to turn users into aero-spoke junkies.

Installation is time-consuming because, depending on the make of hub used, the spoke holes have to be filed or machined into slots. Some manufacturers (e.g. DT Hügi) can supply pre-slotted hubs.

Applications

Road or track with mass-starts or time trials. Many professional racing teams use front wheels with aero spokes all season long. The most popular type of spoke for track racing.

Also used in the mountainbike sector, but primarily for exclusive and luxury models and high-end Sunday morning bikes.

DT Hügi Hub

Butted spokes (reduced spokes)

Double butted (DD) and triple butted (3D) spokes are the favorite components of wheelbuilding professionals. Their advantages enable us to produce durable wheels.

Spokes with reduced diameter arms are not only lighter and more aerodynamic, but, even more important, they have better springing characteristics than straight spokes. They relieve the spoke elbow and the thread and, when under excessive load, react in a similar way to the straining screws used in the machine industry.

Under normal riding conditions these spokes do not spring, the wheel remains stable. If it, however, receives a radial "bump", the appropriate spokes spring to take the load's peaks. When put under extreme pressures, the spokes warp with the result that the wheel will require retruing.

To demonstrate the range of loads that reduced spokes can deal with, a tensioning-warp diagram, compiled by an independent tester is reproduced on page 20. A DT Competition spoke 2.0/1.8/2.0 mm was installed at a tangent - similar to the way it is installed in a wheel - into a hub and then placed under tension at the thread.

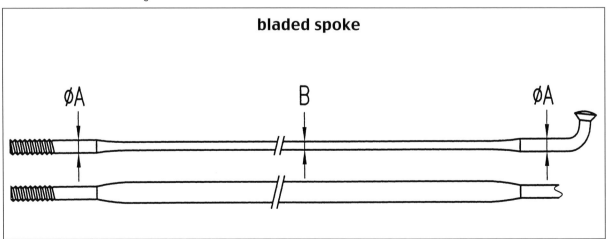

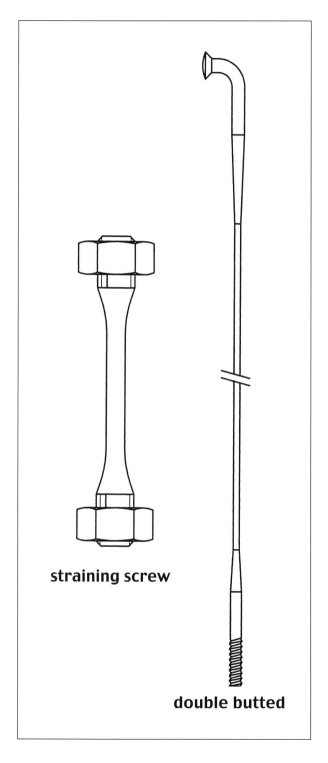

straining screw

double butted

The diagram shows something that many colleagues do not know, namely that:

- On a standard profile rim using round-headed nipples (lower area of the diagram), the spokes can never be damaged by tensioning or tightening. The rim begins to react at a tension of over 1,200 N (270 lbs. tension), it begins to collapse and/or the flanks of the nipple are damaged by the nipple wrench (as though the work has been "botched").

- On rims with a deep V-cross section, using hexagonal nipples, tensioning of up to 2,000 N (450 lbs. tension) can be carried out and yet still have springing capability in reserve (higher durability).

tension-warp diagram

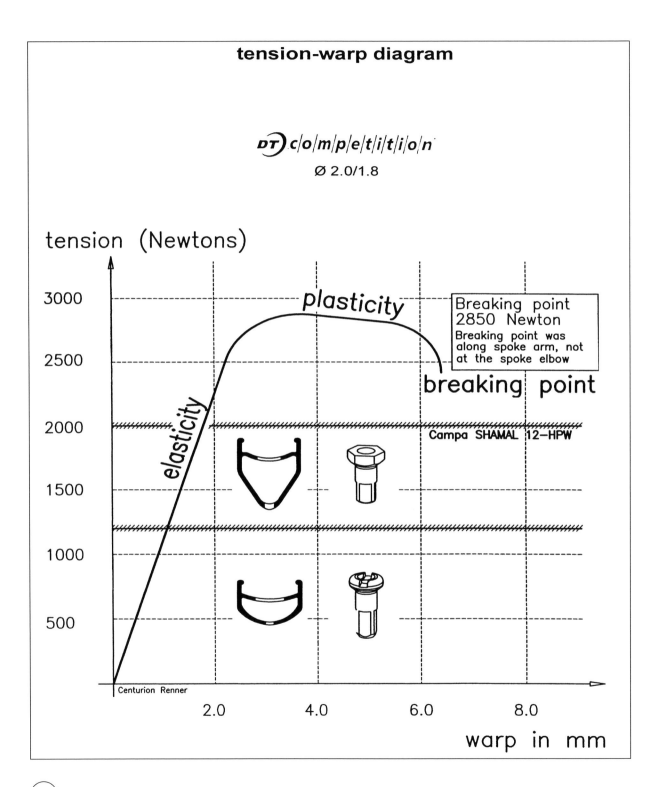

DT competition
Ø 2.0/1.8

tension (Newtons)

3000 — plasticity

Breaking point
2850 Newton
Breaking point was
along spoke arm, not
at the spoke elbow

2500

elasticity

breaking point

2000 — Campa SHAMAL 12—HPW

1500

1000

500

Centurion Renner

2.0   4.0   6.0   8.0

warp in mm

Double-butted spokes

Characteristics:

Same diameter (ØA) at spoke elbow and thread, the spoke arm is, however, reduced in diameter (ØB).

Variations in Diameter		
millimeters		
ØA ———	ØB ———	ØA
2.0 ———	1.8 ———	2.0
1.8 ———	1.6 ———	1.8
2.0 ———	1.5 ———	2.0
1.8 ———	1.5 ———	1.8

Flexible spoke arm, lighter and more aerodynamic than a straight spoke.

Application:

The universal spoke for all types of high quality wheels. The robust (2.0/1.8/2.0 mm) or the lighter type (1.8/1.5/1.8 mm)can be used to cover nearly the entire range of cycling activities:

- Road, track 28″, 26″ and 24″
- Mountainbike Cross (rims and disk brake wheels) City bikes, luxury bikes and Sunday morning bikes - Tandems 26″ and 28″
- Wheelchairs (racing and indoor sports)
- Trekking 26″ and 28″

Triple-butted(3-D) spokes

Characteristics

Three different diameters:

- Largest diameter (A) at the spoke elbow (2.3 mm)
- Mid-diameter (B) at the thread (2.0 mm)
- Smallest diameter (C) along the spoke arm (1.8 mm)

Ideal reinforcement at spoke elbow, flexible arm as on double-butted spokes.

Application:

Specially developed for extreme, problematic applications. Sensible for MTB Cross and Downhill (disk brakes), touring, treking and tandems, because of its robust and yet high springing characteristics.

Also solves wheel problems caused by heavy riders.

Hubs with narrow spoke holes should be drilled out to 2.8 mm depending on the manufacture.

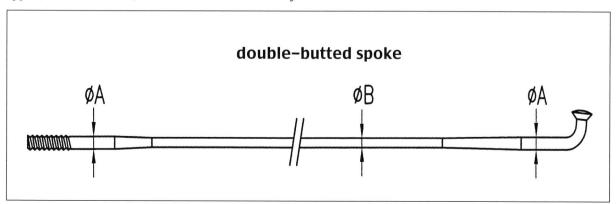

double–butted spoke

ØA   ØB   ØA

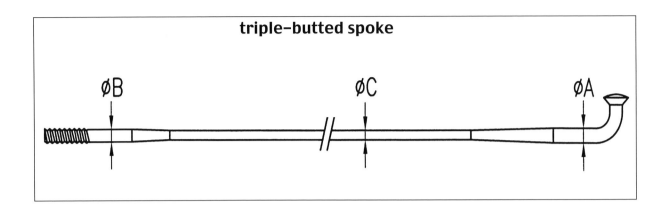

triple–butted spoke

A well-stocked and assorted supply of spokes.

Stock Supply

Type, diameter, length:

In order to work efficiently, wheel builders producing large numbers of handmade wheels need a well thought-out supply of spokes on hand.

My current largest stock is of DD spokes 2.0 / 1.8 / 2.0 mm.

These spokes have, as mentioned above, universal applications. The 2.0 mm spoke elbow and the 1.8 mm spoke arm can cope with higher stresses than the thinner types and, as far as the price/performance ratio goes, they are the leaders.

The lengths of spokes in stock vary depending on the rim currently in fashion. At the moment the lengths on hand are:

- Road 28"   281-284 and 292-302 mm
- Mountainbike 26" 260 - 270 mm

A suggestion would be to stock lengths in steps of 2mm at first, then later in steps of 1 mm.

If a certain length of spoke is not in stock or if unusual lengths are required, knowing how to "dock" a spoke can be useful. Docking is shortening a longer spoke to the length required and then re-cutting the thread. The sensibly priced spoke thread cutter made by HOZAN, model C 915, is ideal for this work.

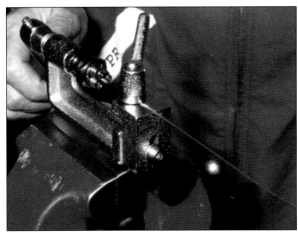

HOZAN C 915

Those who may find docking long spokes too complicated could also save time by using a home-built tool, such as one similar to the one I made myself.

The tool made by PHIL WOOD requires only a cranking movement through 360° to shorten a spoke and cut a new thread. The tool is, however, quite expensive.

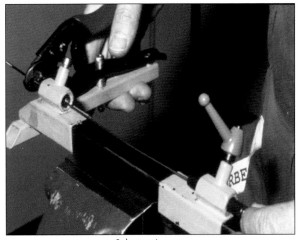

Schraner's own.

Phil Wood's machine.

Spoke reducing roboter. (DT SWISS)

Manufacture

Straight gauge spokes are relatively easy to manufacture. The wire is taken from a spool, is straightened, cut to the correct length and fit with spoke head and elbow and threaded.

Butted spokes require more work. Some manufacturers pull the wire, others opt for a technologically and ecologically unsound principle, namely grinding.

Market leader DT SWISS use their own patented method of cold forging. High speed rotating hammers reduce the diameter of the spoke arm and simultaneously compress the metal structure.

This system results in very precise tolerances in the diameter and circularity, as well as in a homogenous metal structure without a concentration of stress.

On the next page is a simplified diagram of the DT SWISS method of producing tapered and reduced diameter spokes.

Spoke production, head forging and elbow bending. (DT SWISS)

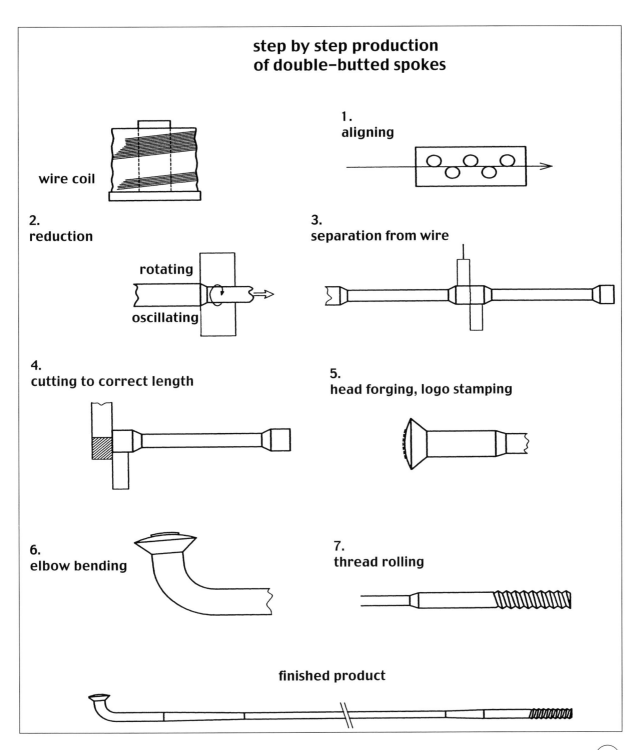

step by step production
of double-butted spokes

wire coil

1.
aligning

2.
reduction

rotating

oscillating

3.
separation from wire

4.
cutting to correct length

5.
head forging, logo stamping

6.
elbow bending

7.
thread rolling

finished product

Materials/Requirements

Of course only so-called stainless steels or even titanium can be considered for the manufacture of spokes for high-end applications.

Market leaders DT SWISS use their very own kind of material for the manufacture of their spokes:

Stainless steel
X 12 CrNi 18/10
Material # 1.4301

which is comprised of:

Approximately 18% chrome
Approximately 10% nickel
Approximately 72% iron and additives

Titanium spokes are made from:
Titanium metal matrix composite - "Beta C".

DT SWISS places extremely high demands on the quality and precision of their suppliers' products. Every single roll of spoke wire is painstakingly checked before delivery.

Stainless steel wire, stocked and ready to produce spokes.

All DT SWISS spokes must pass tests held to the following standards:

DIN 79100 (German Industry-Norm); (European quality standard based on German Industrial Standards, tests held on finished wheels)

JIS (Japanese Industrial Standard); measurements only;

BIS (British Industrial Standard); measurements only.

A special spoke apparently made from carbon fiber proved to be a bit of a flop despite a huge marketing blitz. Inhuman patience was required to insert the spokes to one's satisfaction, an ideal tensioning of the spokes seemed to be impossible and you could even snap the spokes by hand.

Threads and diameters (gauges)

Serious spoke manufacturers roll the thread instead of cutting them.

The advantages are:

- A gentler transition from the thread to the spoke arm

- Compression of material at the thread surface

- Thread diameter is slightly larger, which avoids play between the spoke and the nipple.

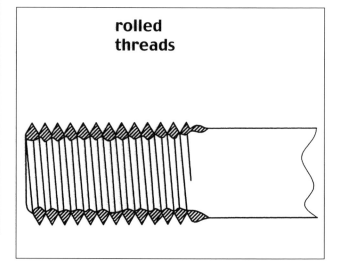

rolled threads

Greatest disadvantage of cut threads is the sharp-edged, possible breaking point at the transition from the thread to the spoked arm.

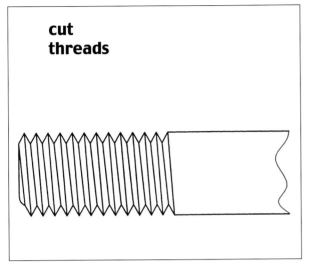

cut threads

Non-English speaking Europe uses millimeters to size their spokes. These sizes relate to the following gauge sizes in English-speaking countries.

Gauges/Millimeters	
G 13	2.3 mm
G 14	2.0 mm
G 15	1.8 mm
G 16	1.6 mm
G 17	1.5 mm

e.g. a double-butted spoke

G 15/16/15 = 1.8/1.6/1.8 mm

The higher the G number, the thinner the spoke

The lower the G number, the thicker the spoke

Weight comparison / Weight savings

I took several sets of DT Swiss spokes which would be the equivalent of those used for a pair of mountainbike wheels (2x 32 pcs 265 mm long) and weighed them. My findings are contained in the diagram on the following page.

Accelerating a bicycle uses power and the amount of power required can be reduced by judicially reducing the weight of components.

Basically, we can place possible weight reduction into two categories:

a) Static weight reduction of parts which are only accelerated in the direction of travel (frame, handlebar, saddle, etc)

b) Dynamic (moving) weight reduction of the rotating wheel in the direction of travel.

The further outward you use lighter parts on a wheel, the greater the dynamic weight reduction!

Light hubs and extremely thin spokes are therefore not really necessary. It would be wiser and more effective to use aluminum nipples, light rims and light tires.

Saving weight by using light spokes alone not only has the advantages, but also disadvantages:

- Excessively thin spokes reduce the load-carrying capabilities of the wheel;

- Insufficient number of spokes require stronger and therefore heavier rims.

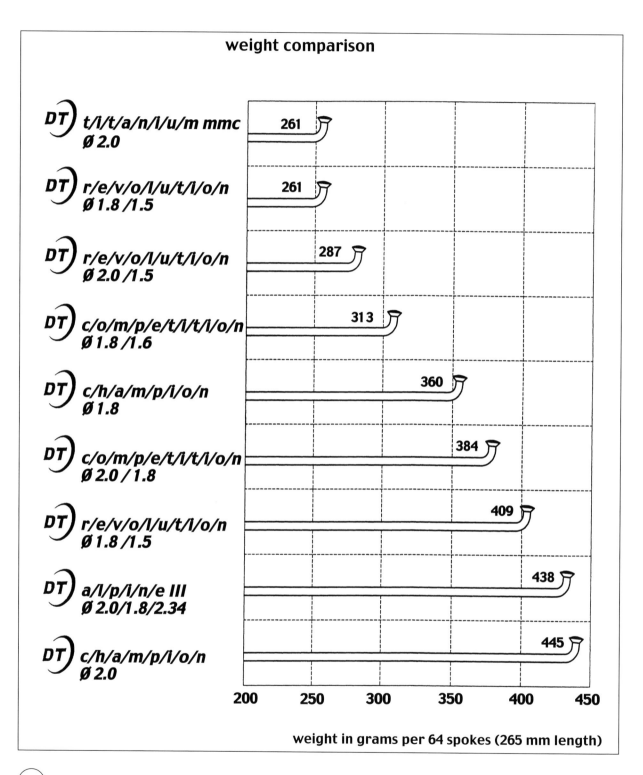

weight comparison

DT) t/i/t/a/n/l/u/m mmc Ø 2.0 — 261

DT) r/e/v/o/l/u/t/i/o/n Ø 1.8 /1.5 — 261

DT) r/e/v/o/l/u/t/i/o/n Ø 2.0 /1.5 — 287

DT) c/o/m/p/e/t/i/t/i/o/n Ø 1.8 /1.6 — 313

DT) c/h/a/m/p/i/o/n Ø 1.8 — 360

DT) c/o/m/p/e/t/i/t/i/o/n Ø 2.0 / 1.8 — 384

DT) r/e/v/o/l/u/t/i/o/n Ø 1.8 /1.5 — 409

DT) a/l/p/i/n/e III Ø 2.0/1.8/2.34 — 438

DT) c/h/a/m/p/i/o/n Ø 2.0 — 445

200 250 300 350 400 450

weight in grams per 64 spokes (265 mm length)

Nipples

Types of nipples

The round-headed nipple is the classic choice for flat cross-section rims.

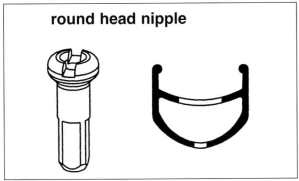

round head nipple

Available from DT SWISS in nickel-plated brass, plain or anodized aluminum and in lengths of 12 (the most popular), 14, 16, 19 and 22 mm. Thread diameter 1.8, 2.0 and 2.34 mm.

Brass nipple flanks, when used with a spoke wrench, can cope with a spoke tension of up to 1,200 N.(270 lbs), those of aluminum up to 1,000 N (225 lbs).

Nipples with hexagonal heads were designed and are used specially for rims with a high V-cross section.

The material is nickel-plated brass and they are available in lengths 12 and 16 mm with a thread diameter of 2.0 mm.

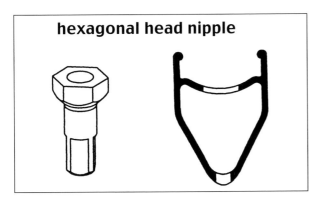

hexagonal head nipple

The hexagonal head, tightened with a 5.5 mm socket wrench, permits extremely high spoke tensioning of up to 2,000 N (450 lbs.) (e.g. CAMPAGNOLO Shamal 12 HPW). One disadvantage is the fact that mostly, the entire nipple is inside the rim and so truing the wheel requires the tire to be removed.

Materials

Brass is the ideal nipple material. The brass alloys used for nipples have both high strength and excellent friction characteristics. Even when the nickel plating is damaged and at extremely high spoke tension, brass nipples chew into neither the spoke nor the rim, whether equipped with eyelets or not.

Aluminum nipples have taken technical leaps over the past few years. Wherever effective weight-savings is required, namely towards the outside of the wheel, aluminum nipples can have huge advantages.

When truing wheels with aluminum nipples, it is important to lubricate the nipple flanks and the transition area of the nipples and the eyelets. A precise, suitable spoke wrench is an absolute must for avoiding damage during this stage.

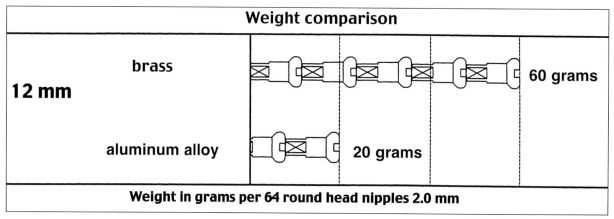

Weight comparison		
12 mm	brass	60 grams
	aluminum alloy	20 grams
Weight in grams per 64 round head nipples 2.0 mm		

Manufacture

Nipples machined from brass and aluminum material are the result of costly work yet, for the wheel professional, they seem to reflect a higher class of quality, in view of the craftsmanship of their manufacture.

Nipples pressed from the same materials are simpler to manufacture and, despite the fact that they are of the same quality of machined nipples, they look "cheaper."

The surface of brass nipples is nickel-plated while that of aluminum nipples is either left as it is, or anodized.

Spoke wrench gauges

For high quality handbuilt or machine-built wheel manufacturing, almost the only nipples used are those suitable for a 3.3 mm spoke wrench, although sometimes 3.4 mm are used for mountainbike wheels. All other nipples are either specially made for bicycle manufacturers, products from the Far East or relics.

Hubs

From the aspect of a manual wheelbuilder, only hubs appropriate for the quality of our products are good enough. Cheap hubs are never considered.

If the client has been given the option of choosing the components, then chances are that he or she,

being influenced by marketing strategies and advertising, will select either a high-end hub made by a market leader or for an expensive one produced for the after-sale market. There are hundreds of products, some of them better quality than those made by the market leaders, some of them which could be honestly described as a "botch".

My personal opinion is that, as far as mountainbikes go, so-called ultralight or tuning hubs are unnecessary, because the weight-savings does not make up for their disadvantages. The hub body are insufficiently torsion resistant   think of sus pension forks and disk brakes -- and the hub flanges are too thin. Sometimes the bedding of the industrial bearing can become stretched by the immense strength of the spoke tensioning, the bearings become loose and begin to rattle.

High quality hubs.

The thickness of the hub flange and the diameters of the spoke holes are of primary importance for a good, durable road or mountainbike wheel. The spoke head and elbow perfectly suit an ideal flange thickness of 3 mm. Mountainbike hubs are all drilled too large, because, in the early days of mountainbiking, only 2.3 mm spokes were used. 1.8 mm and 2.0 mm are the most popular spoke diameter these days, yet the holes were never corrected to fit this size. Cycle manufacturers prefer larger sizes because it makes the job of lacing the spokes into the hub easier. That is the reason why the cheaper the hub, the larger the holes!

Not only the diameter of the hole but also its shape plays an important part. A microscopically countersunk, plain, no-nonsense hole is perfect, permitting the "soft" alloy to bed itself against the pressure points of the spoke.

Follow-up countersinking of the spoke holes of a new hub is a no-no. We old wheelbuilders did it for years because we didn't know any better. Countersinking has the undesired effect of extending the hole diameter.

Spoke holes of over 2.3 mm in the flange are anything but ideal for use with 1.8 mm or 2.0 mm spokes. If no washers are used before the spokes are laced, then the spoke will have a certain amount of play, it will move in the spoke hole every time the load changes, extends the diameter, becomes brittle and breaks at the elbow.

Even the cross sections of the flanges make their own demands. Their flanks should be configured

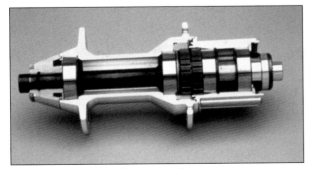

Perfect flange configuration.

in such a way that they help the spokes to run in straight lines across the rim.

Differentiating between a large flange hub and a small flange hub is set at 68 mm, being the diameter of a circle drawn through the center of the spoke holes. Large flange hubs have gone out of fashion, being used today primarily on track racing bicycles for reasons of tradition. They are relics from an age when the quality of the (steel) spokes was very poor and when people tried anything and everything to reduce spoke breakage. Today they are only effective on wheels with 36 quad-crossed or 40 or 48 (tandems) triple-crossed spokes.

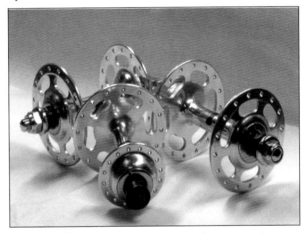

High flange hubs, the one in the center is a "hi-low" hybrid, produced once by Campagnolo and called "Piccolo-Grande".

Today's "large-flanged" disc brake hubs are still counted as small-flanged hubs.

Rims

A wheelbuilder can be master of his trade, but in the end, the quality of his work still depends on the selection of the rim. Rims, even though they are from the same company, the same model and the same quality, still have subtle differences. When they leave the production lines, rims are not radially circular. The rim profile is extruded from flat rod, cooled over rollers, cut to size, turned into the actual rim shape and finally their ends are joined. The rims are often not even perfectly flat.

If you lay a new rim on a flat table, you can often see it see-sawing.

So it is up to us, the wheelbuilders, to put everything in order and, towards the end of the work, the different spoke tensioning required to balance out that particular rim's peccadillos is extremely time-consuming.

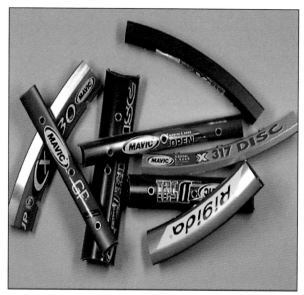

Modern rims used to build custom handmade wheels.

Function

The rims are the two components of a bicycle subjected to the highest loads. During a ride they are pushed and pulled radially and laterally without a trace of the respect they deserve. They have to act as "brake discs" for rim brakes, and as mount devices for the tires. In principle they are a circular, tensioned spring designed to absorb radial and lateral stresses during rides. A deep cross section rim made from good, "hard" material warps for a fraction of a second then returns to its original shape. A rim whose cross section is too shallow and/or is made from a soft alloy is incapable of doing this. The rim retains the bump and when retrued, the spokes in that particular area have too little tension and become instable. The

result is either constantly loose nipples or prematurely broken spokes.

Materials

The steel used for the rims of yesterday's quality wheels has today been replaced by lighter alloys.

For their top-of-the-line products, leading rim manufacturers use only the best alloys with a hardened anodized surface. Many other manufacturers, especially those who are not on top of today's technology, take cheap, excessively soft alloys and simply make the rims attractive by using bright colors.

Rim production may appear to be a simple job, but it needs a huge amount of experience and a lot of know-how. Numerous newcomers and fly-by-nights have been forced to stop production after a short time.

Rim cross sections

It is a matter of principle that rims without a hollow section are never used in the building of high quality wheels. They are too soft and don't have any flexibility.

For extremely stable and durable road wheels, I personally only use warp-free V-cross section rims. They have excellent load carrying abilities, need a low number of spokes (32, 28, 24) and, depending on the manufacture, can cope with spoke tensions of over 1,500 N (337 lbs.).

Rims with standard cross sections are usually sufficient for mountainbike use, but, for extreme situations, high V-profile rims and a reduced number of spokes (28, 24) can be considered.

The wheel geometry on rear wheels, whether they are for the road or off-road, with 8-speed or 9-speed sprocket cassettes, is asymmetrical. It is therefore important to realize that overly shallow rim profiles, popular for their low weight, are insufficiently robust even with 36 spokes. The rear wheel will become unstable and risks collapse.

Opinions are divided on the question whether eyelets are necessary on a rim or not. Eyelets primarily strengthen the spoke hole in the rim. Rims equipped

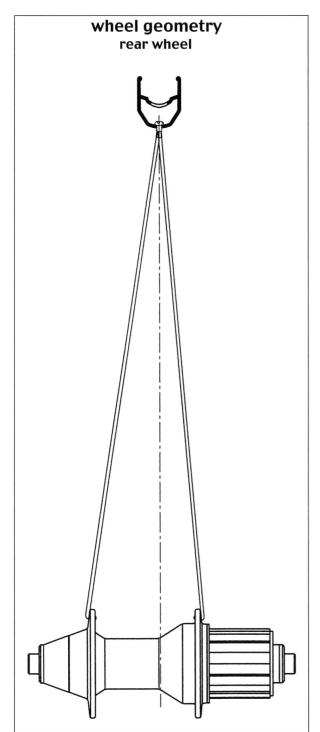

wheel geometry
rear wheel

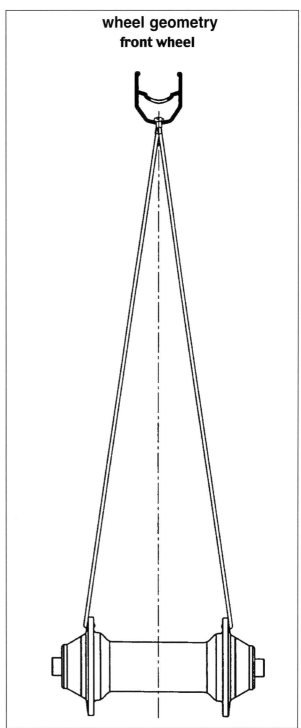

wheel geometry
front wheel

with eyelets are usually heavier than those without, but simply truing the wheels, because the nipples (brass or aluminum on steel) can be trued easier than rims without eyelets (brass or alloy on alloy). On the other hand, rims with badly fitted eyelets can result in a maddening, persistent noise while riding.

Rims without eyelets are as good as any others, as long as the point along the bedding against which the nipple heads butt, have been reinforced. The future will probably belong to rims without eyelets, if only for environmental reasons.

As long as the work has been carried out conscientiously and with precision, welded rim joints are superior to those using a separate joint.

"Mechanically jointed" rims have the tendency to bulge outwards at the joint, when under high spoke tension. The two spokes closest to the mechanical joint must therefore be tensioned higher in order to allow them to retain the shape of the rim. If the joint does not fit precisely or if it is not riveted to the rim, the joint can move during the ride. The unpleasant result is that the brake catches at this particular place and braking becomes somewhat ragged.

Routine work at Six-Days, wheel cleaning and polishing, Bremen, 1982.

Wheel components

rims
popular cross–sections

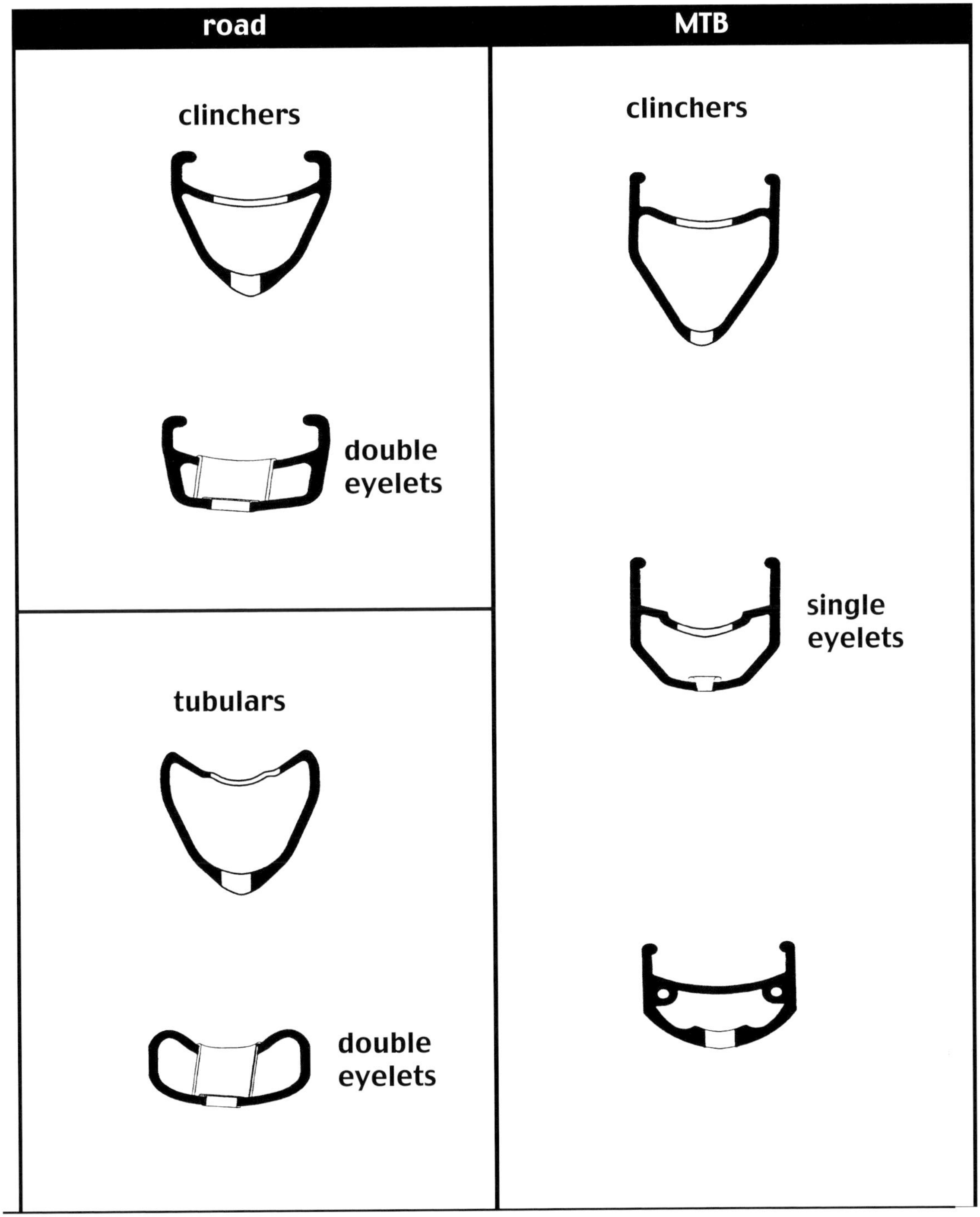

road	MTB

road

clinchers

double eyelets

tubulars

double eyelets

MTB

clinchers

single eyelets

FRITZ BRÜHLMANN

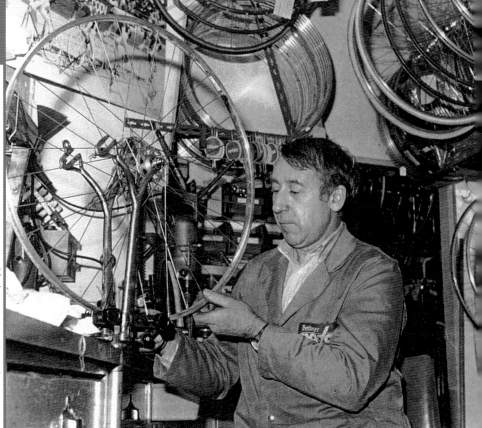

Fritz Brühlmann

Fritz Brühlmann - The institution

Every race mechanic, every current or former track racer knows Fritz Brühlmann, the full-time, professional chief mechanic of the Swiss Cycle Racing Team. His knowledge, ability and experience are legendary. His self-designed and home-made components, gadgets and tools - you could start your own museum with them - are true witnesses of a colleague who carries out his work with professionalism, passion and heart.

As a member of a project team he was co-inventor of the bladed spoke - known today as the aero-spoke. His ideas were put into practice in 1977 in an old village smithy, where a mechanical smith's hammer flattened one spoke after another.

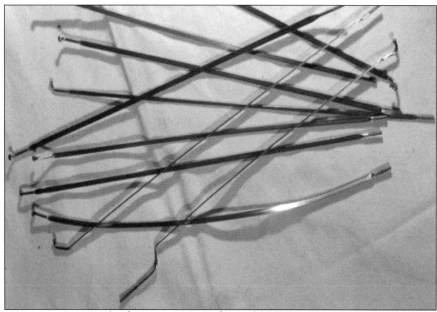

The first attempts to forge bladed spokes.

A lot of expensive press forms were destroyed or had to be modified in those early days, as the quest for a yet more aerodynamic spoke continued. Finally, wind tunnel tests at the ETH (Switzerland's most prestigious Technical University) in Zürich confirmed the improved aerodynamic characteristics of the spokes.

The riders of the Swiss Track Racing Team were the first to ride on wheels using 24 of these aerodynamically effective spokes in the 1977 World Championships in Venezuela. They caused a sensation.

All the time and effort put into developing the spokes

were crowned by Robert Dill-Bundi's Pursuit Olympic gold medal in Moscow, in 1980. His bike was equipped with a 24-aerospoke wheel on the front and - to suit his immense strength - a 28-spoke wheel on the back.

All these spokes had been made by hand, one by one. It wasn't until much later that the production was automated.

Fritz was the person who revived and improved the practice of tying and soldering, an activity which had fallen into disuse. He had spoken to several "old timers," had simplified and improved their methods and sought out gadgets which would make the job easier. It took him years to find the best wire to use for the tying, and that quest alone would make enjoyable reading. He tested and evaluated every possible type of wire of every possible diameter - and the proof of all his tests is still heaped in a huge box full of spools of wire which have proved to be unsuitable. He shares his knowledge with anyone who requires it. He has taught me a great deal about wheel-building, he kept a critical eye on my work and showed a lot of patience during my first attempts at the "Brühlmann Method of Tying and Soldering".

He was and still is the fatherly adviser of many young racers. He played an important role in the careers of the young Risi and Betschart, being the coach for their successes at amateur 6-Days. When he retires in a few years, a great chapter of the race mechanics' history will end and the cycle racing scene will be the poorer for it.

Risi-Betschart, winner of the amateur 6-Days of Zürich 1989 with coach Fritz Brühlmann.

Ivan Gotti - The featherweight

Before the start of the Giro d'Italia in 1997, the people from Cannondale had a feeling that the overall win could well go to the practically unknown hill-climbing specialist, Ivan Gotti. The order was sent down from on high that a standard team bike should be put on a crash diet, so that it would stand on the scales at 7.5 kg. The diet consisted of changes to the frame, lightweight parts and delicately light wheels. The job of making three sets of wheels came to me - it was a dream come true. Cannondale specified which rims and hubs should be used and I chose the spokes.

I selected DT Revolution spokes, 2.0/1.5/2.0 mm, 28 per wheel, double-crossed, tied and soldered on both the front and back wheel, and aluminum nipples.

The wheels survived the grueling Giro without any trouble, so well, in fact, that Francesco Casagrande also used the <u>same</u> wheels for the mountain sections of the Tour de France and the World Championship as well.

Giro Win in 1997.

PART 3

The craftsmanship

The craftsmanship

Spoke Failure

If a spoke ever breaks on a wheel that I have built, then it is due to a fault of mine. Despite using high quality rims, hubs, spokes and nipples, *somewhere*, *somehow* I must have either made a mistake or the failure is due to an oversight. It is never the spoke's fault because:

<u>Spoke failure is *always* caused by an unstable spoked structure being imperfectly balanced in the rim.</u>

One or both of the following causes can lead to spoke failure. Fortunately, we can take prevent-ative measures against both causes when building the wheel.

1. Play between the hub and the spoke.

2. Insufficient spoke tension.

As long as the wheelbuilder understands these two causes and works for their prevention in mind, <u>then he can guarantee that his wheels will never suffer from spoke failure for the lifetime of the rim</u>. This, of course, presumes normal riding conditions. We all know that there are riders who, deliberately or accidently, tend to trash everything they ever use!

A Sunday-morning ride.

Cause #1

Play between the hub and the spoke.

When a bike is ridden, its wheels are placed under radial loads and the rim flattens out a little as it presses against the road surface. Each spoke is therefore placed under load and relieved once every rotation of the wheel.

A wheel which has covered 1,250 miles has been subjected to a million load changes! ... And so a wheel with 32 spokes has been subjected to *32 million* load changes!

The attachment point of the spoke to the hub suffers a great deal during these load changes. If the spoke's head and elbow is seated perfectly in the hub flange, without any play at all, then nothing can go wrong. But if the attachment point has the tiniest amount of play, then you have a spoke failure waiting to happen. Every time the wheel turns, the spoke jumps. A forging, shearing and whiplash effect occurs at the hub flange every time and the spoke hole, which is oversized any-

way, is enlarged. A vicious circle begins, the spoke elbow is subject to huge stresses and the material is changed at an molecular level, making the spoke material brittle. The spoke "gives up the ghost" because it simply can't and won't carry on.

Interestingly enough this often occurs without any warning and rarely when the rider is placing the wheel under particularly high loads, more often than not happening during a leisurely ride. If you look at the spoke closely, you can clearly see how the spoke has been made forged. The area appears polished and the thickness of the spoke has been reduced.

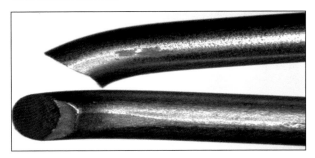

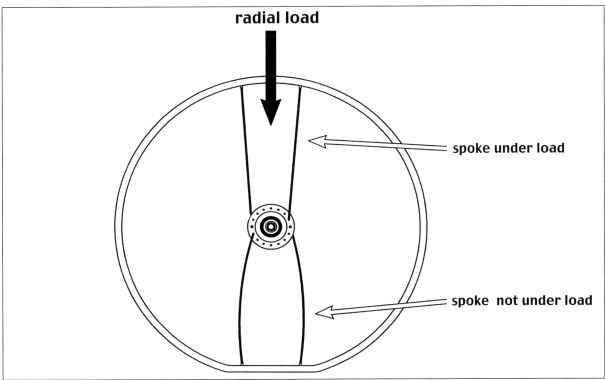

radial load

spoke under load

spoke not under load

The tactile test.

Solution

As I mentioned in a previous chapter, most makes of hubs are equipped with oversized holes in the factory. If spokes have play when attached to these hubs, then they will break when subjected to long term loads. The user then presumes that either the spoke was no good in the first place, or the wheelbuilder didn't do his job properly. Blame everyone, but not the hub manufacturer, right? So it is up to us, the wheelbuilders, to correct the mistakes of those hub manufacturers which means that the solution has to be applied before the problem even occurs.

Spokes with a diameter at the elbow of 2.0 mm are usually used for high quality wheels. The ideal spoke hole diameter in the hub flange is 2.3 mm and this is usually ideal for 2.0 mm elbow diameter.

In order to prevent the play which causes damage to the spokes, professional wheelbuilders use special brass washers (DT Proline), and we always use them when the difference between the diameter of the spoke and the diameter of the hub's spoke hole is greater than 0.3 mm. Of course, it is not necessary to measure this every time a spoke is installed. Just insert a spoke into the hub and move it to see if any play can be detected (tactile test).

If the smallest amount of play can be detected, or when in doubt, use a washer beneath every spoke head. The tension causes the washer to adopt a funnel shape as the washer centers the spoke in the hole . That also increases the thickness of the flange.

If spokes equipped in this manner need to be straightened during lacing, the spoke material is not damaged. And the result is a spoke hub joint which is guaranteed free of unnecessary play.

The rules are therefore:
Always use a washer
 - when there is any tactile play,
 - when using 1.8 mm spokes and
 - when in doubt.
Using washers will slightly reduce the length of the spokes, and this can be compensated by selecting spokes that are 1mm longer.

You seldom see a professional, manually-build wheel without washers. They don't just *shine* like gold, they're worth their weight in gold to the wheelbuilders and riders too!

If a used wheel is returned to the workshop because of repeated spoke failure, then the first thing to do is to loosen all the nipples by two nipple wrench turns, then cut out all the spokes and replace them with new ones, but this time using washers.

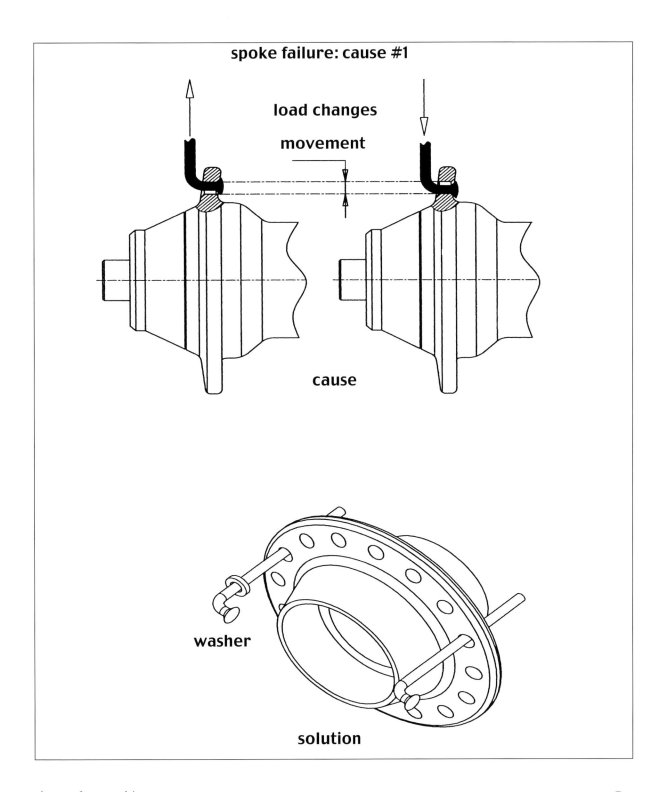

spoke failure: cause #1

load changes

movement

cause

washer

solution

Cause #2

Insufficient spoke tension

The majority of wheels today have insufficient spoke tension. This is chiefly due to ignorance or - as far as machine-built wheels go - for economic reasons, because perfectly tensioned wheels require high quality rims.

During riding, a wheel is placed under different loads. These loads are mostly radial, due to the weight of the rider, bumps in the road, etc. Lateral loads occur in corners when the rider stands up to pedal, while torsional loads occur during acceleration and when braking with disk brakes.

Loose spokes make the wheel imbalanced. The lower the spoke tension, the more the spokes not under load tend to bend. They spend their short lives being bent and stretched, bent and stretched. And even though they may start out with a perfect fit, they begin to move in the spoke hole and, as time passes, this has the same damaging effect of any movement between the rim and the spoke.

Many of my colleagues are of the opinion that high spoke tension itself is damaging. They reduce the tension and finish up with "soft wheels." Well I will put it in writing for you that those spokes are going to break. In addition, wheels like that feel "mushy" to ride and their reaction to the rider is delayed. The wheel is not supposed to be the damper unit of a bike - that's what the tires, or front suspension forks and frames on MTBs are for. A good wheel is only meant to take up the stresses of momentary overloads, such as bumps in the road.

Most spoke failures occur on the left-hand side of the rear wheel, where a lower spoke tension is unavoidable because of the asymmetrical geometry of the wheel. The tension here is about 60 to 65% of that of the drive side on the right.

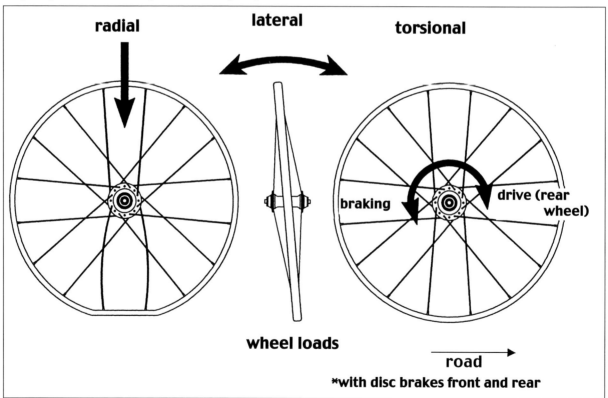

radial   **lateral**   **torsional**

braking   **drive (rear wheel)**

wheel loads

road

***with disc brakes front and rear**

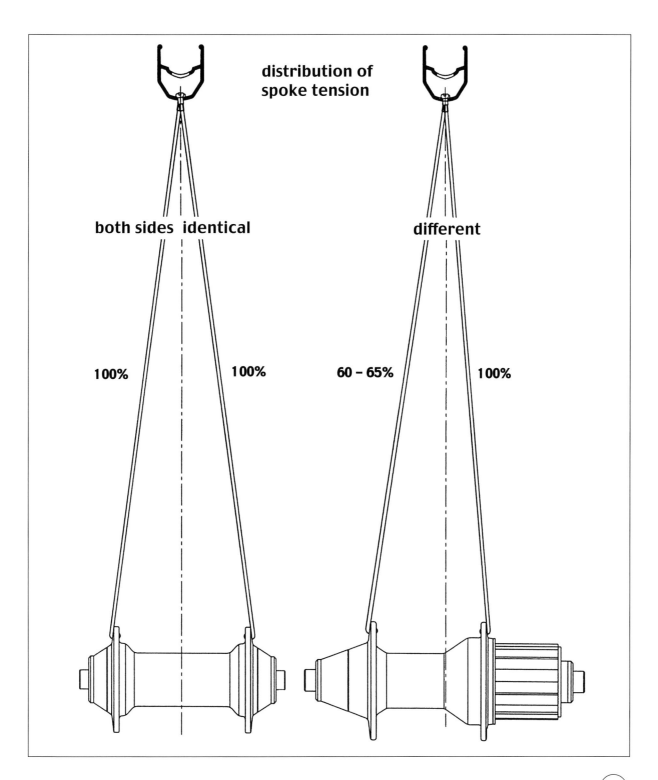

distribution of
spoke tension

both sides identical

different

100%

100%

60 – 65%

100%

If spokes break on the right hand side of the rear wheel, it is because the spoke tension is too weak. An additional negative side-effect and a sign of insufficient spoke tension is when nipples keep coming loose. Nipples have the same function as nuts on bolts. Nuts also become loose if they are insufficiently tightened, or haven't enough torque. Nipples will not come loose and nipple retainers are unnecessary on a well-tensioned wheel *if* the rim cross section has the correct dimensions.

Solution

High spoke tension helps to balance the wheel when it is under load. The spoked structure will hardly move at all.

When the wheel is overloaded, the spokes under the most load get support by the neighboring spokes, but only with high spoke tension. Loose spokes can hardly support themselves, let alone their neighbors!

The higher the spoke tension, the more effectively the overload is distributed over several spokes.

If the wheel is momentarily radially overloaded, the uppermost two spokes are subject to extremely high tensile loads. Correct tension does not only allow the close neighbors, but all other spokes in the upper half of the wheel, to act as damping units.

The perfect spoke tension is determined by the quality of the rim. For this reason, the highest possible tension for flat rims is lower than that for high V-cross section rims. And on cheap rims made from soft aluminum, you can forget any kind of respectable spoke tension altogether.

It is also important to know that you can never tension a spoke (using round or hexagonal head

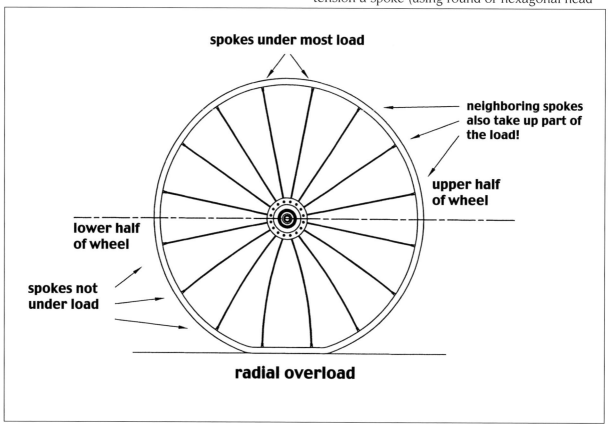

nipples) so highly that it breaks. Before that point is reached, either the four corners of the nipple will be "rounded" by the nipple wrench or even the best and strongest rim will twist out of shape into a "potato chip".

So-called "soft wheels" can be trued fairly quickly, but they will soon start to cause headaches.

True, a well-tensioned wheel means more work. The spokes tend to twist much more under the high torque, which means that the stress-relieving procedure has to be repeated several times. The work of truing gets more difficult and requires more time. But the result is still a professionally-built wheel which will "stand" and which will avoid yet any more work in the future.

So how high is this perfect spoke tension?

On the most popular standard hollow section rims (MAVIC 317, 517, 321, 521, Open Pro), the average torque according to my experience is:

> 900 - 1,000 Newtons on the front wheel (200 - 225 lbs)
>
> 1,000 - 1,100 Newtons on the right-hand side of the rear wheel (225 - 250 lbs) and only
>
> 600 - 700 Newtons on the left-hand side of the rear wheel (135 - 160 lbs)
>
> (1 Newton = 0.2248 lbs.)

The tension of the spokes on the left-hand side of the rear wheel cannot be increased because we're already at the limit on the right. If we were to try and increase the tension, the rim would be pulled out of the wheel center towards the left.

On rims with high V-cross sections (CAMPAGNOLO Atlanta, RIGIDA DP 18 and 22), and when using hexagonal nipple heads, spoke tension can be as high as 1,500 Newtons (340 lbs.).

Spoke tension can be measured either by feeling by hand or by using your experience, or by using a spoke tension meter, often called a tensiometer.

The amount of spoke tension that a rim can take can be quickly judged when, while at the end of

the truing and tensioning work, the wheel demonstrates odd behavior. The more you correct the truing, the more it distorts. The tension is too high and the rim is trying to collapse. In this case, relieve the tension by one-half or three-quarters of a nipple turn per spoke and re-true the wheel. If you have a tensiometer, measure the ideal values and note the results for any future work on the same type of rim. That will save a lot of time in the future - you'll just need to measure the tension now and again during the truing stage until the ideal tension, which you noted before, has been reached.

I worked for years without a tensiometer, being under the false impression that instinct and experience were enough. Then I bought one of the first HOZAN tensiometers on the market and started making comparisons. Shamefacedly I had to admit that my super instinct was not so super after all. Even my mood on any particular day gave different results. Since then I work with a tensiometer

A portion of the author's tool bench.

and it is always at hand next to the truing equipment. While truing a wheel, I make a check now and then and get closer to the perfect tension step-by-step.

Measurements are only carried out on two or three spokes and then I take the average of those figures. So measuring every single spoke of a wheel is by no means necessary. There will always be a slight difference between the tensions of one spoke and another (+/- 50N) (11.25 lbs), because even the best rim on the market isn't perfectly circular when it leaves the factory. It is up to us wheelbuilders to correct the circularity by truing the wheel.

Tying and soldering can also bring additional balance to the spoked structure. The idea behind tying and soldering, as well as the procedure are explained in the chapter "Tying and Soldering".

Wheelbuilding

Selection of Spokes and Nipples

It should be obvious that, for high quality wheels, only butted, DD or 3-D spokes and machined nipples should be used. Bladed or aerospokes can be used in special cases

For modern wheels with 8 or 9 speed cog sets and in view of the resulting disadvantageous wheel geometry, we wheelbuilders have to consider several factors when selecting the type and diameter of spokes, as well as the nipple material.

The spokes placed under the most load are those on the drive side of the rear wheel. The rider sits in an almost vertical line above the spokes, and the power he puts into the pedals is transferred directly to the rim via these spokes. There is therefore no sense in using thin, light spokes here.

After several unfortunate experiences and subsequent tests, I now build rear wheels, be they for mountainbike or for the road, using at least double butted 2.0/1.8/2.0 mm spokes on the drive side and - also very important - brass nipples. I

simply refuse to use finer spokes or even aluminum nipples here.

The spokes on the left-hand side of the rear wheel are practically only for show. When the wheel is radially overloaded the necessary low tension and steep angle of these spokes do little to take up the load. The only support they give is to lateral stability, so that the wheel does not simply flip over.

For light V-braking mountainbike wheels I can, from personal experience, recommend the following spokes and nipples. (See diagram on next page.)

If one, for example uses colorless, neutral aluminum nipples for the front wheel as well as for the left-hand side of the rear wheel on such a pair of wheels, then the differing kinds of nipples (brass and aluminum) can hardly be told apart. One could, however, use colored nipples on one side of the front wheel, colorless on the other side and then use the same colored nipples on the left-hand side of the rear wheel.

Although braking using rim brakes places the spokes under hardly any load, wheels with disc brakes make high demands on spokes. The braking forces are transferred from the hub to the rim via the spokes !

For this reason, DD spokes finer than 2.0/1.8/2.0 mm have no business on wheels with disc brakes. In the more extreme area of Downhill, 3-D spokes (2.3/1.8/2.0 mm) and only brass nipples are much more suitable.

In general, double butted spokes with a midsection of under 1.5 mm should not be used on high quality wheels. They begin to stretch and twist even before the ideal spoke tension has been reached.

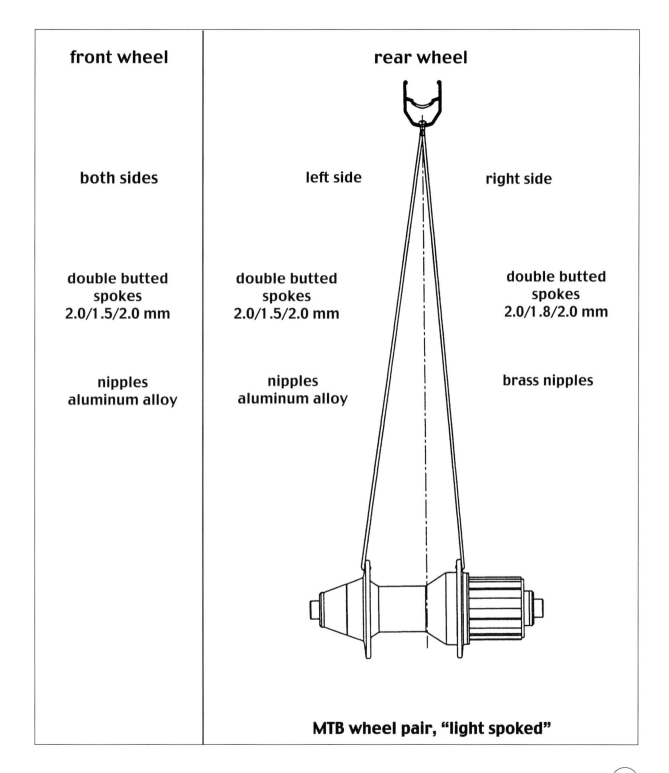

front wheel

both sides

double butted
spokes
2.0/1.5/2.0 mm

nipples
aluminum alloy

rear wheel

left side

right side

double butted
spokes
2.0/1.5/2.0 mm

double butted
spokes
2.0/1.8/2.0 mm

nipples
aluminum alloy

brass nipples

MTB wheel pair, "light spoked"

Spoke Lengths

When we speak about spoke lengths, we always mean the distance between the inner edge of the spoke elbow and the end of the spoke

The selected spoke length is correct when, on a finished wheel, the end of the spoke is in line with the top of the nipple head.

If the spokes of a shallow rim are too long or if they extend over the top of the nipple head, they could damage the rim tape and tube.

If the spokes are too short the nipple head could be torn off under extreme circumstances. This is also the reason why nipples from respectable manufacturers have threads all the way down the nipple head.

Utilizing the whole thread of a correctly dimensioned spoke helps to support the hard-working nipple head. We mechanics simply abhor too short or extending threads.

Working out the correct spoke length used to be a game of chance. Time-consuming, complicated formula were hardly ever used and, instead, you just selected a certain length according to your experience and - if you were lucky - you got it right first time. On bad days you spent ages trying and testing two or three other lengths. But lately there's been a small boom in this area. Numerous systems using a pocket calculator or a personal computer take all the headache out of the job and get it right every time. Even so, the most important dimensioning step, namely the rim diameter, is often neglected. Yet, only by using the point at

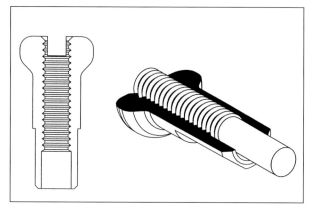

which the nipple head butts against the rim as a dimensioning factor, can precision be maintained.

Other measuring methods, in which various rim cross section thicknesses are a factor are more complicated and often less precise.

I have tested numerous calculation systems. I always prefer the simplest and finally settled on two quite inexpensive systems: the Spoke Length Calculation Table, SPOKE CALC from DT SWISS and the French PHILAMY pocket calculator.

The former comes as a 50 x 70 cm poster which I stuck onto the back of my workshop door. It is easy to use, clearly explained and, with a bit of practice, you can calculate the correct spoke lengths within two or three minutes. An example of the chart is shown on pages 52 and 53.

The second system, developed by Derrick Coetzer is pre-programmed in a CASIO FX-6300G pocket calculator.

spoke length

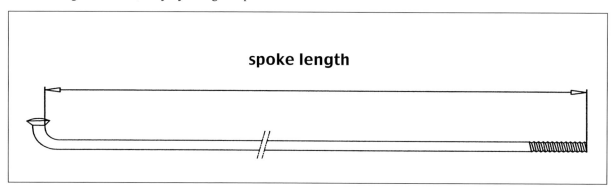

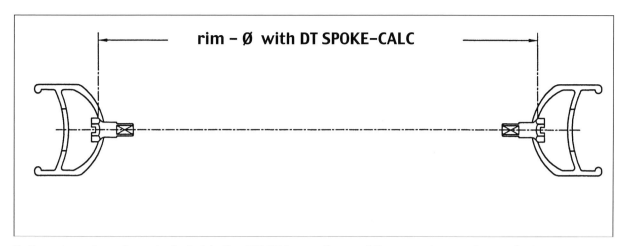

rim – Ø with DT SPOKE-CALC

Both systems have been included in the DT PRO-LINE catalog at my suggestion.

I should not need to mention that once you've determined the correct spoke length you should make a note of it for future use.

Check the rim diameters you have listed from time to time, because some rim dimensions, even those of the same type and manufacture, can often vary.

The SPOKE-CALC measuring nipple should never be inserted directly next to the rim joint because this will result in a false rim diameter. The illustration on the opposite page is based on my own experience and shows the variation of spoke lengths for different methods of lacing.

SPOKE-CALC ™
by BPP and DT

Abstract of original chart;
without explanations

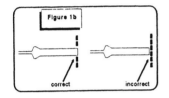

STEP 1. SIZE THE RIM

RIM SCALE

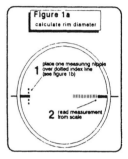

STEP 2. CALCULATE HUB CENTER-TO-FLANGE DIMENSION

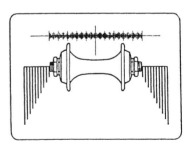

STEP 3. CALCULATE HUB FLANGE DIAMETER

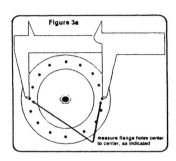

Figure 3a

measure flange holes center to center, as indicated

TABLE A

HUB CENTER-TO-FLANGE DIMENSION

RIM DIAMETER

RIM DIA.	15 16 17	18 19 20	21 22 23	24 25 26	27 28 29	30 31 32	33 34 35	36 37 38	39 40 41	42 43 44 45
586	293 293 293	294 294 294	294 294 294	294 294 294	294 294 294	295 295 295	295 295 295	295 295 295	296 296 296	296 296 296 296
587	294 294 294	294 294 294	294 294 294	294 294 294	295 295 295	295 295 295	295 295 296	296 296 296	296 296 296	296 297 297 297
588	294 294 294	295 295 295	295 295 295	295 295 295	295 295 295	296 296 296	296 296 296	296 296 296	297 297 297	297 297 297 297
589	295 295 295	295 295 295	295 295 295	296 296 296	296 296 296	296 296 296	296 297 297	297 297 297	297 297 297	298 298 298 298
590	295 295 295	296 296 296	296 296 296	296 296 296	296 296 296	297 297 297	297 297 297	297 297 297	297 298 298	298 298 298 298
591	296 296 296	296 296 296	296 296 296	296 297 297	297 297 297	297 297 297	297 297 298	298 298 298	298 298 298	298 299 299 299
592	296 296 296	297 297 297	297 297 297	297 297 297	297 297 297	298 298 298	298 298 298	298 298 298	299 299 299	299 299 299 299
593	297 297 297	297 297 297	297 297 297	297 298 298	298 298 298	298 298 298	298 298 299	299 299 299	299 299 299	299 300 300 300
594	297 297 297	298 298 298	298 298 298	298 298 298	298 298 298	299 299 299	299 299 299	299 299 299	300 300 300	300 300 300 300
595	298 298 298	298 298 298	298 298 298	298 299 299	299 299 299	299 299 299	299 299 300	300 300 300	300 300 300	300 301 301 301
596	298 298 298	299 299 299	299 299 299	299 299 299	299 299 299	300 300 300	300 300 300	300 300 300	301 301 301	301 301 301 301
597	299 299 299	299 299 299	299 299 299	299 300 300	300 300 300	300 300 300	300 300 301	301 301 301	301 301 301	301 302 302 302
598	299 299 299	300 300 300	300 300 300	300 300 300	300 300 300	301 301 301	301 301 301	301 301 301	302 302 302	302 302 302 302
599	300 300 300	300 300 300	300 300 300	300 301 301	301 301 301	301 301 301	301 301 302	302 302 302	302 302 302	302 303 303 303
600	300 300 300	301 301 301	301 301 301	301 301 301	301 301 301	301 302 302	302 302 302	302 302 302	303 303 303	303 303 303 303
601	301 301 301	301 301 301	301 301 301	301 302 302	302 302 302	302 302 302	302 302 303	303 303 303	303 303 303	303 304 304 304
602	301 301 301	302 302 302	302 302 302	302 302 302	302 302 302	303 303 303	303 303 303	303 303 303	304 304 304	304 304 304 304
603	302 302 302	302 302 302	302 302 302	302 303 303	303 303 303	303 303 303	303 303 304	304 304 304	304 304 304	304 305 305 305
604	302 302 302	303 303 303	303 303 303	303 303 303	303 303 303	304 304 304	304 304 304	304 304 304	305 305 305	305 305 305 305
605	303 303 303	303 303 303	303 303 303	303 304 304	304 304 304	304 304 304	304 304 305	305 305 305	305 305 305	305 306 306 306
606	303 303 303	304 304 304	304 304 304	304 304 304	304 304 304	305 305 305	305 305 305	305 305 305	306 306 306	306 306 306 306
607	304 304 304	304 304 304	304 304 304	304 305 305	305 305 305	305 305 305	305 305 306	306 306 306	306 306 306	306 307 307 307
608	304 304 304	305 305 305	305 305 305	305 305 305	305 305 305	306 306 306	306 306 306	306 306 306	307 307 307	307 307 307 307
609	305 305 305	305 305 305	305 305 305	305 306 306	306 306 306	306 306 306	306 306 307	307 307 307	307 307 307	307 308 308 308

TABLE B

HUB DRILLING AND LACING PATTERN   (0=radial)

HUB FLANGE DIAMETER

	24 HOLE HUBS					28 HOLE HUBS					32 HOLE HUBS					36 HOLE HUBS					40 HOLE HUBS					48 HOLE HUBS					
	0	1	2	3	4	0	1	2	3	4	0	1	2	3	4	0	1	2	3	4	0	1	2	3	4	0	1	2	3	4	
30	16	14	9	1	+6	16	15	10	4	+2	16	15	11	6	1	16	15	12	9	4	16	15	13	9	6	16	15	14	11	8	30
31	17	14	9	1	+7	17	15	11	4	+2	17	15	12	6	1	17	16	13	9	4	16	16	13	10	6	16	16	14	12	8	31
32	17	15	9	1	+7	17	16	11	5	+3	17	16	12	7	1	17	17	13	9	4	17	16	14	10	6	17	16	15	12	8	32
33	18	15	9	1	+7	18	16	11	5	+3	18	16	12	7	1	18	17	13	9	4	17	16	14	10	6	17	17	15	12	9	33
34	18	15	9	1	+7	18	17	12	5	+3	18	16	13	7	1	18	17	14	9	4	18	17	14	10	6	18	17	15	13	9	34
35	19	16	10	1	+8	19	17	12	5	+3	19	17	13	7	1	19	18	14	10	4	18	17	15	11	6	18	18	16	13	9	35
36	19	16	10	1	+8	19	17	12	5	+3	19	17	13	7	1	19	18	15	10	4	19	18	15	11	6	19	18	16	13	9	36
37	20	17	10	1	+8	20	18	13	5	+3	20	18	14	7	1	20	19	15	10	4	19	18	16	11	7	19	19	17	14	10	37
38	20	17	10	1	+9	20	18	13	5	+3	20	18	14	8	1	20	19	16	10	4	20	19	16	12	7	20	19	17	14	10	38
39	21	18	11	1	+9	21	19	13	5	+4	21	19	14	8	1	21	20	16	11	4	20	19	16	12	7	20	20	18	14	10	39
40	21	18	11	1	+9	21	19	13	5	+4	21	19	15	8	1	21	20	17	11	4	21	20	17	12	7	21	20	18	15	10	40
41	22	18	11	1	+9	22	20	14	5	+4	22	20	15	8	1	22	20	17	11	4	21	21	17	12	7	21	21	19	15	11	41
42	22	19	11	1	+10	22	20	14	5	+4	22	20	15	8	1	22	21	17	11	4	22	21	18	13	7	22	21	19	15	11	42
43	23	19	11	1	+10	23	21	14	5	+4	23	21	16	8	1	23	21	17	11	4	23	21	18	13	7	22	22	20	16	11	43
44	23	20	12	1	+10	23	21	15	5	+4	23	21	16	9	1	23	22	18	12	4	23	22	18	13	7	23	22	20	16	11	44
45	24	20	12	1	+10	24	21	15	6	+4	24	21	16	9	1	24	22	18	12	4	23	22	19	13	8	23	22	20	16	11	45

Rules of thumb for spoke lengths*

Example: Rims MAVIC X517 (DT Ø 542 mm)
Hubs DT–HüGI MTB, 32 holes
Spokes crossed 3 times

Indication from DT Spoke–Calc	front wheel	rear wheel nondrive side	rear wheel drive side
	265	265	263

	divergences		
	front wheel	rear wheel nondrive side	rear wheel drive side
radial	−14 (251)		
crossed 2 times	− 7 (258)	− 7 (258)	− 7 (256)
28 holes	+ 3 (268)	+ 3 (268)	+ 3 (266)
36 holes	− 3 (262)	− 3 (262)	− 3 (260)
Pulstar	+ 4 (269)	+ 4 (269)	+ 4 (267)

* no responsibility

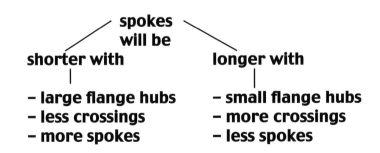

spokes will be

shorter with
– large flange hubs
– less crossings
– more spokes

longer with
– small flange hubs
– more crossings
– less spokes

Number of Spokes

The selection of the number of spokes greatly influences the life expectancy and the strength of the wheel.

The more spokes used, the more stable the w h e e l. The classic upper limit - classic because it has proven itself time and time again over the years - is 36 spokes. Track racing bikes often have 40 and tandems have 40 or even 48 spokes per wheel.

Thanks to the high quality of today's rims and spokes, 32 spokes per wheel are usually sufficient for mountainbikes and road bikes.

Fewer spokes reduce weight and improve the aerodynamic qualities, but need to be given a higher tension which, on the other hand, require more stable, and thus heavier, rims. The weight advantage of fewer spokes is therefore lost on the rims. Fewer spokes improve the aerodynamics but - and this is an important point - only from speeds of 50 kmh (30 mph) upwards.

More spokes mean that the wheel is more stable not only radially but also laterally. When a rider stands up to pedal uphill, for example, the wheel reacts more directly to his pedaling power. A wheel with less spokes feels "spongy".

The higher the number of spokes, the better the simultaneous uptake of overload by the spokes!

Experience shows the following number of spokes for stable and durable wheels:

In case of doubt, always use a higher spoke count.

Number of spokes

		front wheel	rear wheel
MTB 26"	Cross (V-Brake) Disc Brake Downhill Disc Brake	28+32 32+36 32+36	32 32+36
Road 26" and 28"	Race Trekking, Touring, City	24-32* 36	28-32* 36

* dependent upon type of use and of rim (cross section)

Are 24 Spokes Enough?

In 1995 the test team of the Swiss bike magazine *Move News* wanted to find out some definite facts about the most reliable, minimum number of spokes on a mountainbike wheel using rim brakes.

They gave me a free hand for the building of the wheel. The only condition was that the wheels had to survive some very tough off-road and trekking tests.

I took up the challenge using wheels built using two sets of 24 DT Revolution spokes 2.0/1.5/2.0 mm, brass nipples and - in order to counteract the loss of stability through so few spokes, RIGIDA DP 22 high V-profile rims. The drive side of the rear wheel was equipped with the somewhat more robust DT Competition 2.0/1.8/2.0 mm spokes.

The weight of the wheels compared favorably with robustly built 32-spoke wheels.

The wheels ran the gauntlet of the entire *Move News* crew. Thousands of miles offroad and down-hill, as well as a 1,000 mile bike tour (with a lot of luggage), down the Californian coast presented no problem at all. The wheels needed no adjusting afterwards and they're still "standing".

They're still on the wall of the magazine's test workshop, still look very good, thank you, and have become something of an object of desire for visitors. And they're still used from time to time.

The author as track race mechanic, ready to go, Zürich 1988.

The craftsmanship

Spoke patterns

Wheel spokes can be laced in a radial or tangential pattern. Radial spokes project in a straight line from the hub to the rim. Tangential spokes lie tangentially to the flange and cross over one to four adjacent spokes.

Radial Spoking

Competent wheelbuilders use a radial pattern only on rim-braked front wheels, because, in contrast to the rear wheel, there is no torque to be transmitted and therefore no torsion takes place.

It is, however, important to note that this spoking pattern causes the flange to be placed under extremely high radial loads. In addition, the risk of hub flange failure on wheels with more than 32 spokes is greatly increased.

All hub manufacturers give no guarantee for radially spoked wheels!

When applying radial spoking, it is unimportant whether the spoke heads are configured to turn inwards or outwards. The current fashion is to turn them outwards and all spoke length calculation systems are based on this configuration.

The advantages of radial spoking are insignificant, Only the sight of the wheel as it rotates is fascinating. There is no aerodynamic advantages to be gained. All spokes, no matter their lacing pattern, have to withstand the airflow in the vicinity of the rim, where the rotational speed is at its highest. And although radial spoking requires shorter spokes, the weight-saving is hardly worth mentioning.

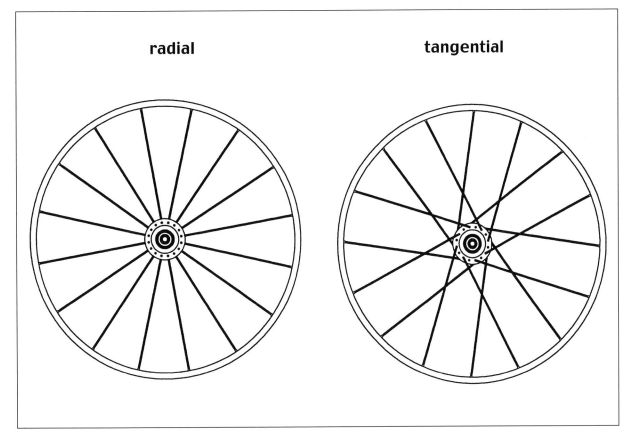

radial   **tangential**

Tangential lacing patterns

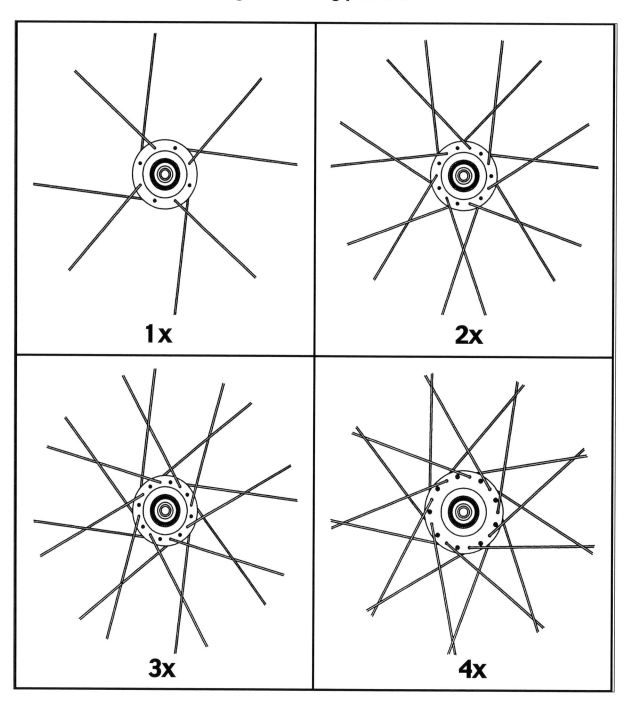

Tangential Spoking

Tangential, crossed spoking is the only option wherever driving and braking forces need to be transmitted from the hub to the rim. The more angled the spokes lay in respect to the flange, the more directly the driving and braking forces can be transferred. The ideal configuration is when an imaginary line, drawn from the axle to the spoke head, forms a right angle to the spoke.

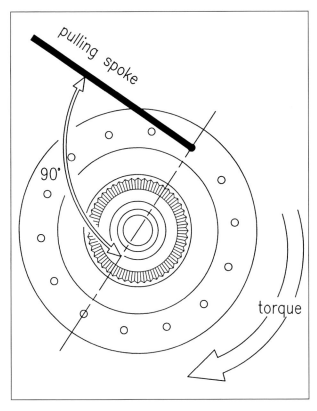

Under torsional loads, radially laced spokes try to adapt to these loads by bending tangentially to the flange. The constantly changing loads cause imbalance to the spoked structure and the result is broken spokes or loose nipples.

For these reasons, radial spoking should *never* be used on a disk-brake equipped front wheel or on any rear wheel.

Yet despite these valid and scientifically-supported arguments, there are still some well-known manufacturers of compact wheels, who apply radial spoking to the rear wheel. They are only correct in doing so when the wheels have deep-V-cross section rims. These permit high spoke tensioning up to 2,000 N (450 lbs), thus avoiding the radial spokes' tendency to align themselves tangentially.

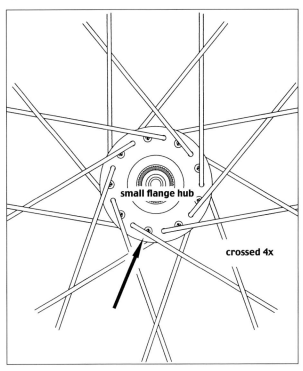

Triple-crossing has proved itself to be very successful on stable, handbuilt wheel using 36 spokes for both front and rear wheels, and can therefore be termed the "classic pattern." Quad-crossed spokes are ideal for large flange hubs, but not for small flange hubs, because every spoke would tend to lie on the head of the adjacent spoke.

Double, triple, and quad-crossed spokes are always additionally interlaced at the outer crossing points. This has two main advantages. It results in a certain damping effect and gives more clearance between the derailleur and the spokes on the drive side of the rear wheel.

Hybrid-Spoking (Crow's foot)

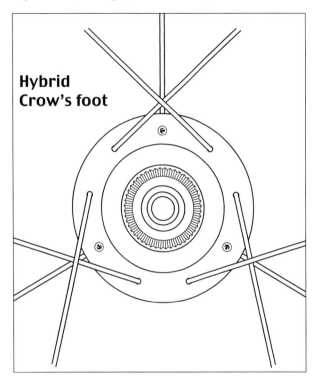

Hybrid
Crow's foot

The crow's foot pattern is somewhat exotic and combines radial and tangential spoking. Of three adjacent spokes, the central spoke is radial and the outer spokes are tangentially laced. This, however, can only be applied on wheels with spokes in multiples of six, for example 18, 24 or 36-spokes per wheel.

It is a very old lacing method and was nearly forgotten in the mists of time, but today, especially for wheels with V-cross section rims and aero-spokes, it has come back into fashion.

Twisted Spoking

The twisting of spokes, instead of the classic crossing work, is a waste of time for road use. Tests have shown that it results in a very unstable wheel. The lateral stability is about the same as a normally spoked wheel, but, radially, the wheel reacts so sluggishly that encounters with momen-tary radial overloads (bumps in the road) the highly praised damping effect is delayed.

The exercise is only useful for trial sport, where the bike is momentarily held at a standstill after hard landings and hopping tricks.

Twisted spoking patterns are not only unaesthetic but are an additional mechanical disadvantage resulting from the extreme angle of the spoke directly at the nipple.

Every serious wheelbuilder who has ever practiced this kind of spoking pattern has sworn to refrain from repeating the error.

Yet, young bike freaks, apprentices and mechanics seem to like this kind of spoking pattern. My advice: Leave them at it and let them continue to show their enjoyment and enthusiasm in this way. It's better to see them rolling spokes than rolling joints.

Twisted spoke pattern.

To answer to the often-posed question concerning where and how many spokes should be inter- laced, the following table should be of assistance.

lacing patterns / applications

number of crossings	front wheel	rear wheel	
		left side	right side
0 / radial road	x	x*	
1 x road	x	x*	x*
2 x road	x	x	x
3 x road, MTB's city–, touring–, trekking–bikes	x	x	x
4 x for large flange hubs only	x	x	x

* only for rims with high cross sections

Identical Symmetry / Mirror Image Asymmetry

The spokes of a rim-braked wheel can be inserted in such a way that the left and right sides are identical to one another or as mirror image opposites. The configuration has no effect whatever on the quality or durability of the wheel.

Pulling spokes/Braking spokes

The spokes under the most stress are the pulling spokes on the drive side of the rear wheel. These have to cope with the permanently-occurring radial forces to the wheel and in addition have to transfer the rider's pedal force.

Personally, I insert the spokes in such a way that their spoke heads are within the flange. I simply have the feeling that this gives these over-stressed spokes a gentler, healthier angle in relation to the rim.

Disk-braked wheels are another matter. Both the front and the rear wheel have "braking spokes" which, similar to the pulling spokes on the drive side of the rear wheel, are put under tensile loads when the rider applies the brakes. Here again, I give the spokes a gentler angle by inserting them with their heads within the flange.

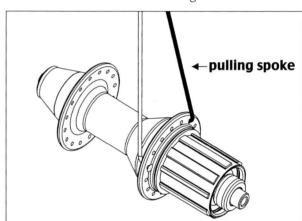

←**pulling spoke**

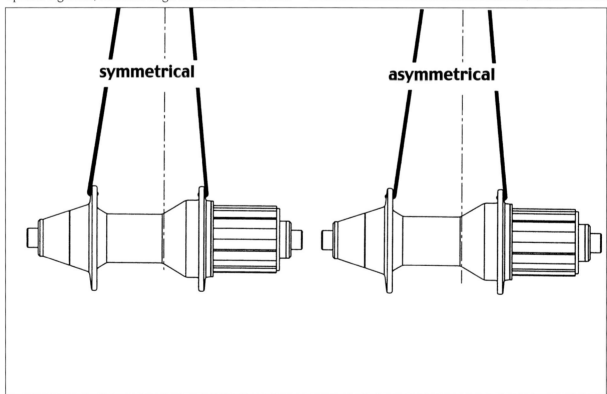

symmetrical   **asymmetrical**

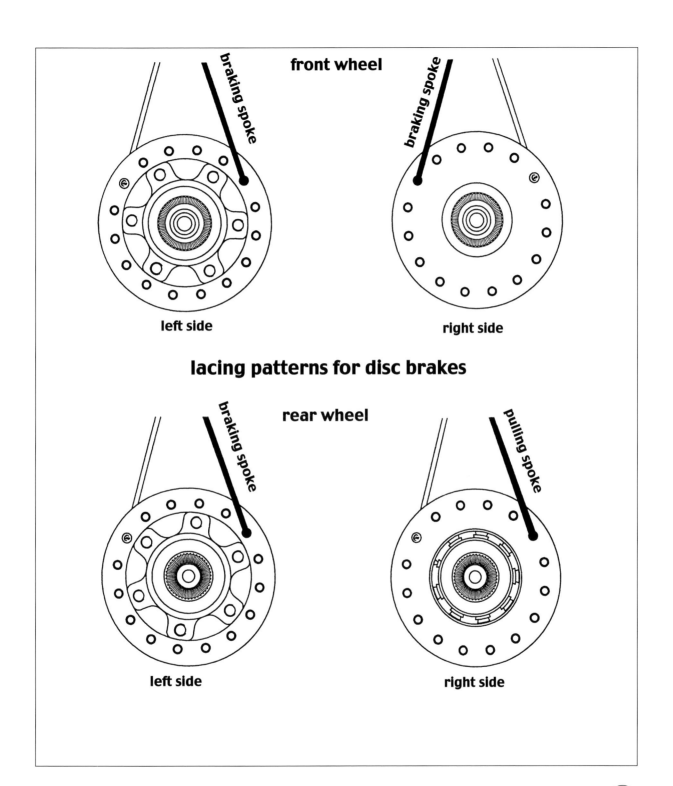

front wheel

braking spoke

braking spoke

left side

right side

lacing patterns for disc brakes

rear wheel

braking spoke

pulling spoke

left side

right side

Pulling spokes with the heads within or outside the flange, identical spoking, mirror image spoking - these are always on the agenda of wheelbuilder seminars and bicycle shows. Everyone thinks they know better but none of them can prove it.

I spent five years of trial and error testing all the various configurations on the wheels of the professional Swiss Team Helvetia-La Suisse and I didn't notice a single difference, despite the fact that all 200 wheels of the team covered over 300,000 miles per year. Despite these tests and evaluations we never experienced a single spoke failure, nor indeed any other problem with the wheels. The decisive factor of the wheels' success was always the stability and balance of the spoking structure. In other words, I used the best, highest tension possible. There was no clearance between the hub and spokes, and I used nothing but double-butted spokes!

Spoking

Preparing the components

Rims

Most rim products - even high end items - are never really finished when they leave the factory. An example is the valve hole, which is seldom burred. We wheel professionals, forever aspiring to the perfection of the art, carry out this small job ourselves, using a 90° burring tool.

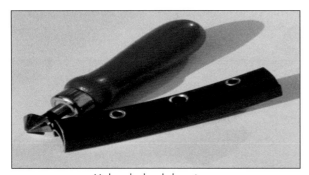

Valve hole deburring.

Nipple holes smaller than 4.3 mm on non-ferruled rims are drilled out, in order to ensure while truing that the nipples can turn easier when they are centered and in order to keep them in line with the spokes. If the nipple holes in this type of rim were not deburred in the factory, this should be subsequently carried out where the nipple head butts against the rim. If this area is not deburred, the nipples - especially aluminum ones - can become distorted under high spoke tension.

Whether from ignorance or a lack of practical experience, many rim manufacturers still make the valve holes in tubular rim beds too small. The result is that the valve area of the tubular lays incorrectly against the valve hole. Every time the wheel turns the tubular causes an unpleasant bump. It is quite difficult to drill out a valve hole and so we solve this problem by countersinking the hole.

Having to do all these little jobs can be annoying. I always do it on batches of five rims before I start any other jobs, just to get it done. Thank heaven for battery-driven, low speed hand drills, which are wonderful for fiddly jobs such as these.

Countersinking the valve hole for tubulars.

The craftsmanship

Hubs

Before spoking, non-anodized hubs should be polished. This also especially applies to hubs which have previously already been spoked. It's a small but rewarding job, because a carefully built wheel with nice, new, shiny spokes looks wonderful, but a greasy, dull hub simply looks awful.

Spokes and Nipples

Every mechanic worth his salt oils the thread of every screw before fitting it. The same applies to our profession when fitting spokes.

An old method, still popular with many of my colleagues is to dip the spoke thread into linseed oil. The linseed oil lubricates the thread during the truing stage. When dry, the oil reverts to its hard, resin-like state and secures the nipple. SpokePrep from WHEELSMITH is made from modern chemicals and works in a similar, but better way.

As far as I am personally concerned, I pour common bicycle oil over the threads, place the spokes on a piece of cloth which soaks up the excess oil and begin spoking.

The exterior of aluminum nipples should be sprayed with oil before spoking begins. They can then be moved much easier during the tensioning stage.

The threads of titanium spokes do not have the same glide characteristics as those made of stainless steel. If brass nipples are used, a high quality oil with teflon additive (SUPER LUBE) or molybdenum additive is usually sufficient. Aluminum nipples are easier to work with on titanium when you use an anti-seize compound (FINISH LINE Ti-Prep) instead of oil.

Tools

The only tool we do not need for the spoking job is the nipple wrench.

During spoking, tighten the nipples so that one turn of the spoke's thread is still visible. In this way, all spokes are "the same length" when the spoking is done, which will simplify the beginning of the truing stage.

Beginners can work with a standard screwdriver. Experienced mechanics use a so-called nipple-driver. This is basically an off-set screwdriver with a rotating handle (BICYCLE RESEARCH USA / DT PROLINE). Professionals prefer a special type of screwdriver head, a "bit." This is equipped with an adjustable pin which unlocks the bit as soon as it comes into contact with the end of a spoke. It is installed into a hand-drill or into the chuck of a battery-powered low speed drill.

Inserting the nipple into deep V-profile rims is difficult. By using a special nipple holder (ULLMANN DEVICES / DT PROLINE), the nipple can be inserted effortlessly into the rim and removed again.

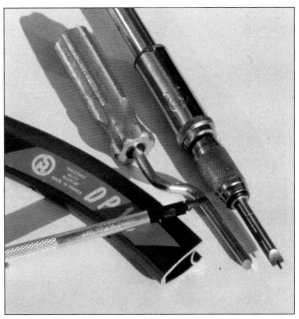

Spoking tools, from left nipple holder ULLMANN DEVICES, nipple driver BICYCLE RESEARCH, hand drill VAR with bit.

Spoking Methods

The method of spoking used does not influence the quality of the finished wheel !

Classical method

This spoking method, described so often in the bicycle press does not need to be described in this book too. A very instructive video by a young American colleague, Garret Traylor, is available for those who are interested in learning this method. The video "Bicycle Wheel Building 101" explains in simple, step-by-step examples how a wheel is spoked, trued and dished. The video is highly recommended for beginners. It can also be found in the DT PROLINE product list, as well as in many wholesaler and retailer stores (30 min. English, NTSC or PAL TV systems).

Schraner's Method

This method of spoking may, at first glance, appear to be somewhat bizarre, yet it is very simple to learn and is simple to teach. The various methodical steps make the work clear and you never lose track of "where you are". One side of the wheel is completed first, the wheel is then turned over and the other side is done equally methodically.

Using this method you always know exactly where you are, should you become distracted. And if you make a mistake during spoking you can see it immediately and the error is therefore simple to correct.

The illustrations on the following pages demonstrate my technique.

Video "Bicycle Wheel Building 101"

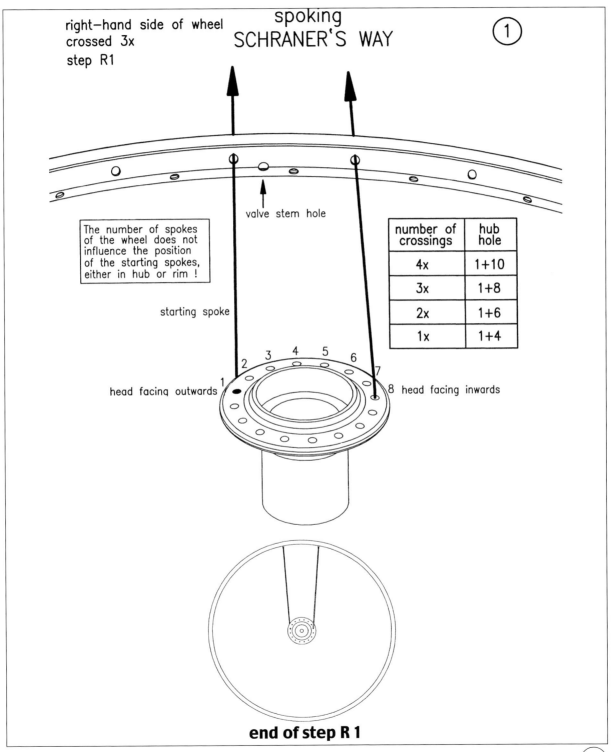

right—hand side of wheel
crossed 3x
step R1

spoking
SCHRANER'S WAY

①

valve stem hole

The number of spokes
of the wheel does not
influence the position
of the starting spokes,
either in hub or rim !

starting spoke

number of crossings	hub hole
4x	1+10
3x	1+8
2x	1+6
1x	1+4

head facing outwards

head facing inwards

end of step R 1

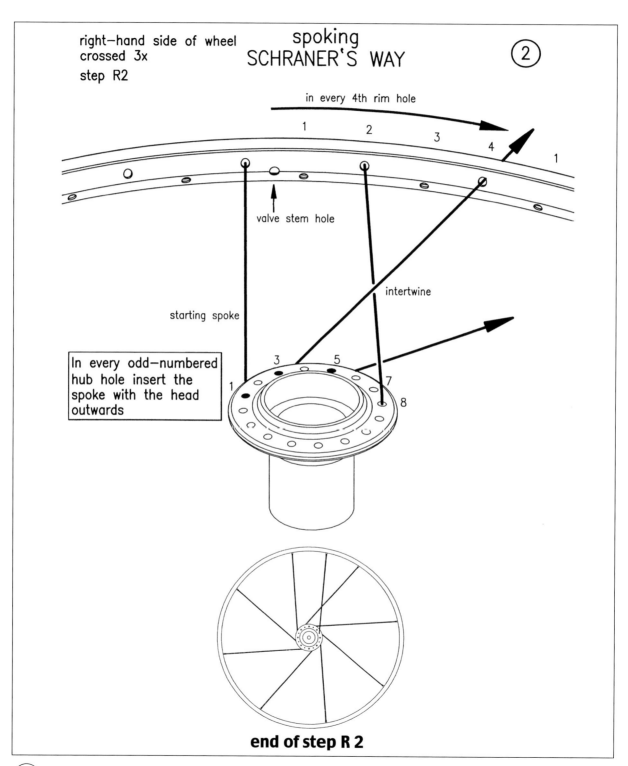

right—hand side of wheel
crossed 3x
step R2

spoking
SCHRANER'S WAY

②

in every 4th rim hole

1   2   3   4   1

valve stem hole

intertwine

starting spoke

In every odd—numbered
hub hole insert the
spoke with the head
outwards

3   5

1   7   8

end of step R 2

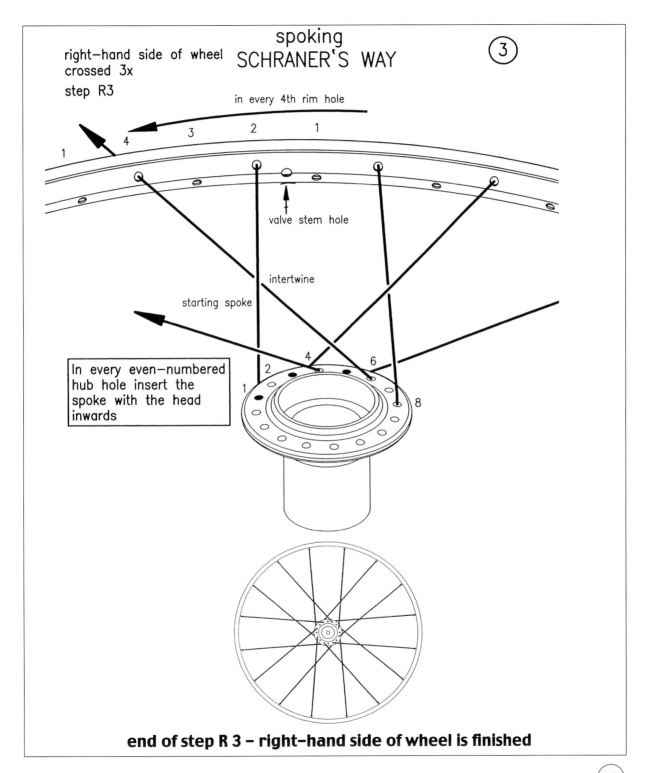

right–hand side of wheel
crossed 3x

step R3

spoking
SCHRANER'S WAY

③

in every 4th rim hole

3 2 1

4

1

valve stem hole

intertwine

starting spoke

In every even–numbered
hub hole insert the
spoke with the head
inwards

4

2

1

6

8

end of step R 3 – right–hand side of wheel is finished

left–hand side of wheel
preparation

spoking
SCHRANER'S WAY

4

step L1

starting spoke of the
right–hand side of the wheel
starting spoke of the
left–hand side of the wheel
1
2
3
4
5
end of step R 2
start with the hub hole
to the right of the centerline

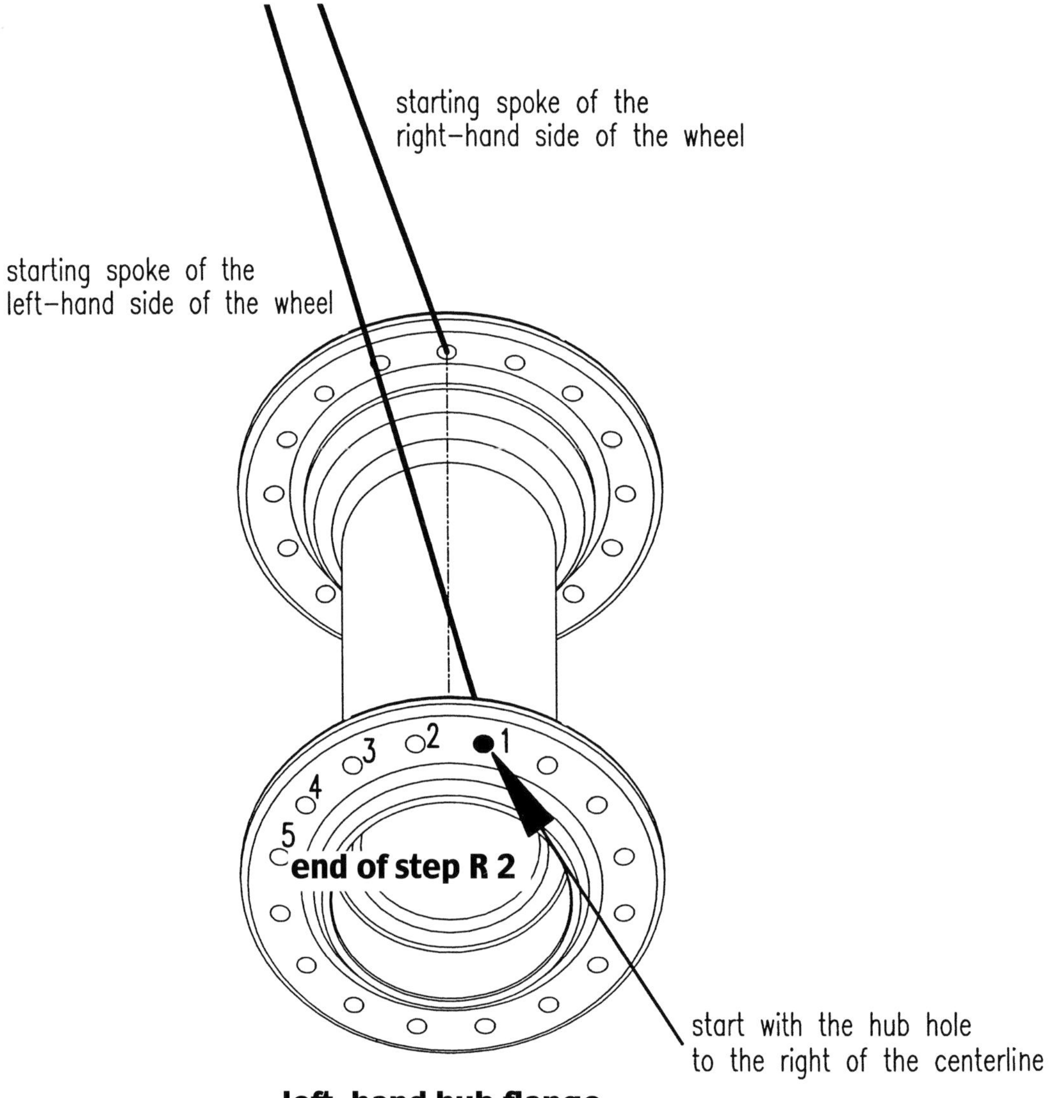

left–hand hub flange

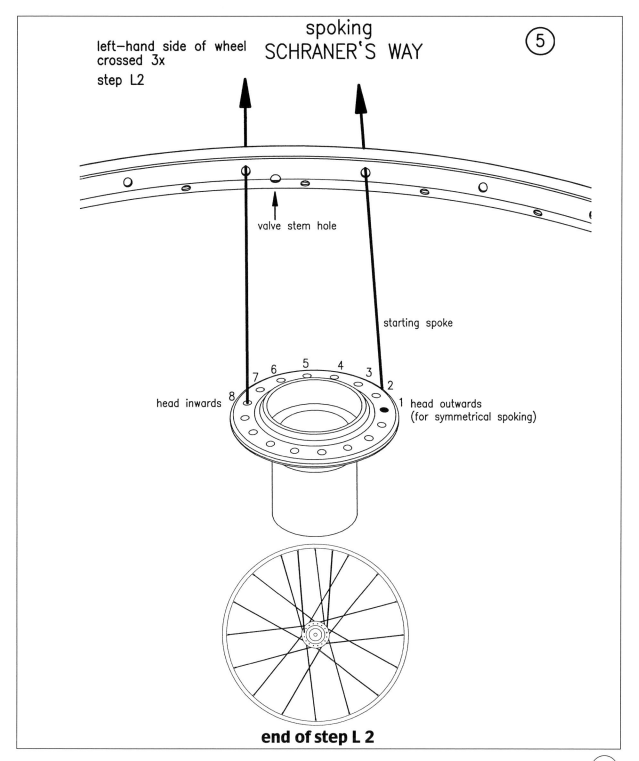

spoking
SCHRANER'S WAY

left—hand side of wheel
crossed 3x

step L2

⑤

valve stem hole

starting spoke

7 6 5 4 3

8 head inwards   2

1 head outwards
(for symmetrical spoking)

end of step L 2

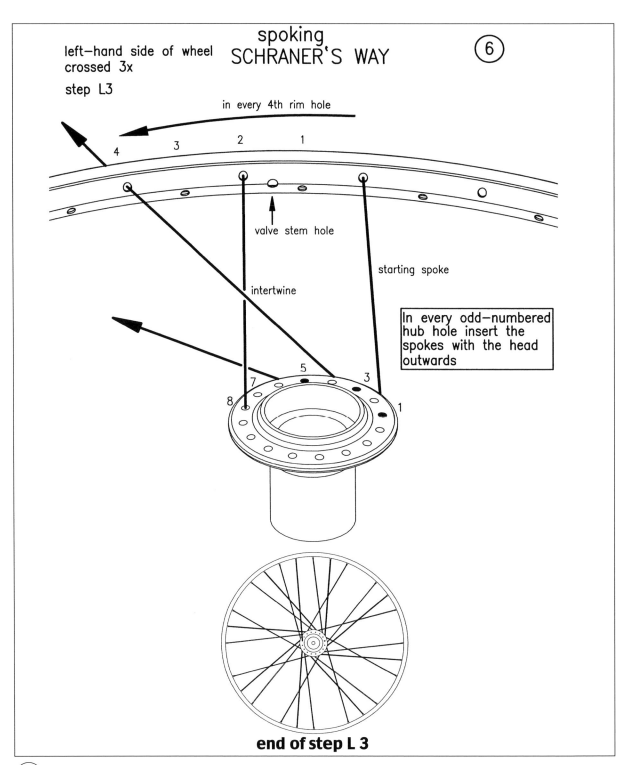

spoking
SCHRANER'S WAY

left–hand side of wheel
crossed 3x

step L3

⑥

in every 4th rim hole

4   3   2   1

valve stem hole

intertwine

starting spoke

In every odd–numbered hub hole insert the spokes with the head outwards

5   3
7
8   1

end of step L 3

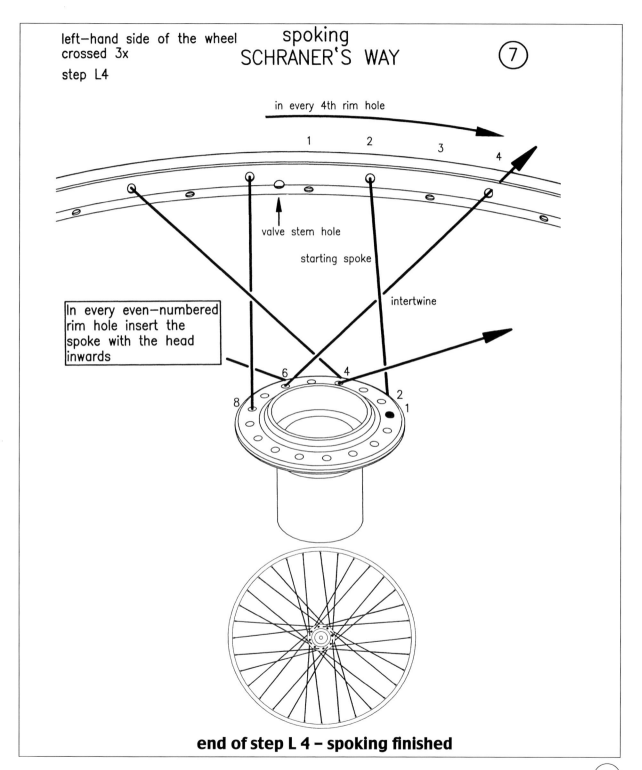

left—hand side of the wheel
crossed 3x

step L4

spoking
SCHRANER'S WAY

⑦

in every 4th rim hole

1   2   3   4

valve stem hole

starting spoke

intertwine

In every even—numbered
rim hole insert the
spoke with the head
inwards

6   4

8   2 1

end of step L 4 – spoking finished

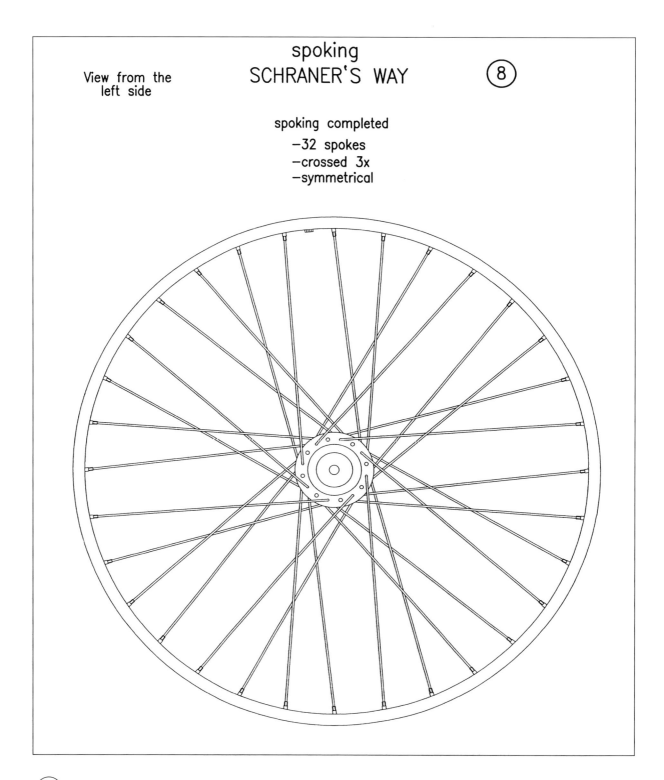

spoking
SCHRANER'S WAY

View from the left side

spoking completed

—32 spokes
—crossed 3x
—symmetrical

Spoking

Before and during the spoking, professionals make sure that, on both wheels of a bicycle, all the manufacturer's rim stickers are correctly visible from the same side.

The company logo near the rear wheel hub is correctly placed by the manufacturer, but, as far as the front wheel goes, it is up to us to spoke a wheel in such a way that the logo on the hub is legible from the rider's viewpoint. The positions of logos on disk-braked front wheel hubs are also predetermined by the manufacturer's recommendations.

Wheel professionals go one step further - when fitting clincher tires they also take care that the tire logos are visible from the same side as the rim stickers. The tire is also installed in such a way that the logo is centered above the valve. One exception to this unwritten rule are mountain bike tires with special profiles, which, for reasons of grip, have to be installed in a special way according to the manufacturers' recommendations.

So, by applying this small detail, it is obvious from a distance that a serious pro who loves his job, was at work here.

Before starting spoking, make sure that:

- the number of spoke holes are the same on both the rim and the hub,

- the spokes all have the correct length,

- the spoke threads have been oiled or otherwise lubricated or prepared and

- that the exterior of aluminum nipples have been sprayed with oil.

Spoking is a comfortable job if you are sitting at the work bench. Arrange the spokes and nipples close at hand.

It is up to you to find your own, most comfortable methods of handling and holding the rim, hub, spokes, nipples and tools. Newcomers could do it with an extra pair of hands, but after a bit of practice you'll settle down into a faster routine.

Scratched rims enhance neither the look nor the professionalism of a wheelbuilding job. Scratches occur when a spoke currently being laced catches the rim. To prevent this from occurring, hold the spoke in your fist and cover the end of the spoke with your thumb. This simplifies the threading of spokes through or around crossed spokes.

When the spoking stage is complete and before the work of truing the wheel is begun, the spokes must be as straight as possible between the hub and the rim. Use the shaft of a screwdriver to press each spoke crossing nearest the rim, towards the hub. You can see clearly how the spokes find the shortest way by themselves.

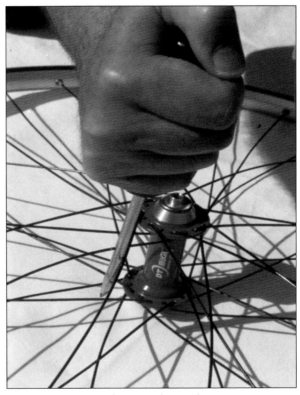

Prealigning the spokes.

Daily routine at Six-Days Races.

I learned how to true a wheel using an old bicycle front fork and my fingernail to measure the misalignment.

Of course that was in the old days and people today are able to buy a wide range of truing stands for everyone from beginners to fully-blown professionals. A good truing stand should be stable enough to support wheels of all axle diameters and hub over lock nut dimensions from 100 to 135 mm, and up to 145 mm for tandem wheels. The sensor should not have any play when it touches the rim. It doesn't matter whether you measure the lateral and radial misalignment using an optical sensor (using a light gap or dial gauge), or audibly by listening for a grazing sound. It is a matter of what you get used to.

The new, inexpensive T 3175 Exact truing device from TACX is recommended for beginners and mechanics with little practical experience. PARK TOOLS, on the other hand, have come up with their new, highly professional TS3, optionally with or without dial reading, which fulfills the requirements of the most demanding wheelbuider. We professionals have had to wait a long time for a tool like that.

Many years ago, out of true desperation to own a truing stand suitable for a professional, I actually built one on my own. But looking at today's technology, I recommend you save your time and energy and go out and buy one!

Truing the wheel

Tools

Wheel Truing Stands

It is always the wheelbuilder who makes a good job of truing wheels, not the truing tools. It is therefore not necessary to have the latest high-tech, sophisticated toy to attain a high quality wheel.

Truing stand TS3 3175 Exact from TACX

Truing stand TS3 from PARK TOOLS.

Schraner's own.

Spoke wrenches

It is difficult to compare the various makes of spoke wrenches. Every wheelbuilder I know has his own favorite.

I have some colleagues whose trusty old spoke wrenches are battered and worn by years of use, yet they still manage to build good wheels without damaging the nipples. Their tools have a certain dignity about them - their handles, shiny from handling, their edges worn from so much hard, but satisfactory work. You would never be able to convince them of the advantages of buying a different, apparently better product. I might even say that you can almost judge the professionalism of a wheelbuilder just by looking at his personal spoke wrench.

An assortment of good spoke wrenches.

The current market leaders are the products manufactured by PARK TOOL and DT SWISS. Every one of these spoke wrenches has only single jaws. Nipples used in jaws of 3.3 mm (0.13″) are the norm in high quality wheelbuilding. The additional purchase of a multi-spoke wrench with several different jaw sizes is however recommended.

Spoke head punch

In principle this is nothing other than a conical punch with a concave point which fits exactly against the spoke head.

As I have previously mentioned, the hub and the spoke should form a solid joint. A solid fit of the spoke head in the flange is therefore an important factor.

At the beginning of the truing stage, when the spokes have already been tensioned somewhat, the spoke head punch (DT Proline) and a light hammer (100g head weight) is used to drive each spoke head into the flange. The rear of the spoke head buries its way in, thus forming a perfect fit and, furthermore, the spoke head butts flat against the flange. This little job doesn't take much time but it will greatly enhance the life of the wheel.

Nothing points to an unprofessional piece of work more than spoke heads pointing every which way in the flange of a handbuilt wheel.

Setting the spoke heads.

Tensiometers

There are not very many manufacturers of tensiometers. In my opinion, the best two on the market are the expensive product made by HOZAN and the approximately $100 WHEEL-SMITH tensiometer, the latter offering the best price:performance ratio. The HOZAN tool is very robust and is suitable for workshops in which wheels are built on a daily basis. The WHEEL-SMITH product is amazingly precise, is somewhat simpler in construction, smarter but is perhaps less robust for tough everyday use.

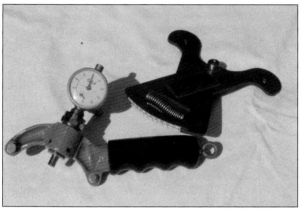

Tensiometers by WHEELSMITH and HOZAN.

All tensiometers function using the same principle. The spoke being measured is fixed at two points, placed under a standard load and the deflection is measured.

Spokes of different diameters deflect differently under the same load. A diagram which is included with tensiometer allows for this and the figure given by the tensiometer is the tension of the spoke measured in Newtons (N).

Truing

This is the final stage of the wheel which has at this point "only" been spoked.

Before the wheel can really "stand":

- the radial and lateral misalignment of the must be corrected

- the spokes have to be correctly tensioned and

- the rim has to be dished.

The final result will be a durable unit comprising of the hub, rim, spokes and nipples. The finished wheel should remain stable while being ridden and yet produce enough elasticity to cope with excessive load. And, in order to avoid spoke failure, the spoke structure should be firm when placed under all loads.

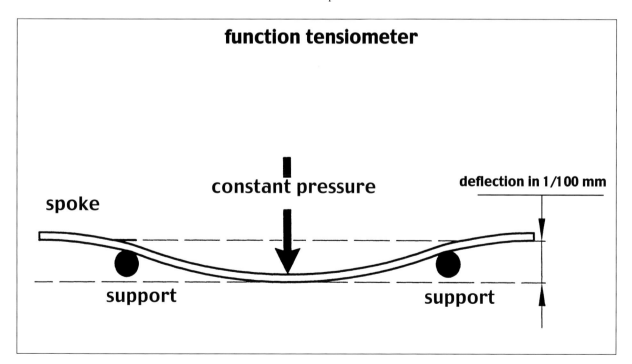

Working with wheels demands a certain ordered discipline. Among other things this means that the wheel should always be in visually the same position as it is when installed in the bike. For example, during every job - including truing - the freewheel on the rear wheel should be on the right, and the brake disc of the front wheel should be on the left. Thus, when truing or centering a rim, we always know whether the correction should be made to the left or to the right.

Truing a wheel is purely a matter of experience. Beginners should gain experience by trial and error, by loosening and tightening spokes and seeing the effect. Patience, perseverance and self-criticism are important criteria.

Mountainbike wheels that are 26-inch are simpler to true than larger diameter 28-inch road wheels. A drop of oil between the rim eyelet and the neck of the nipple greatly simplifies the work of tensioning and truing.

The hub bearings, when clamped into the truing stand, should rotate easily but without play.

The most fastidious work, truing.

Absolute tolerances in the circularity of wheels are often discussed and compared in wheel tests in the bicycle press. Rules and comparisons are nonsensical, because the tolerance of circularity of a finished wheel depend on:

1. The quality of the rim, specifically:

   - the workmanship, especially the joint (welded or plugged) and

   - the quality of the rim profile (tolerances) and the hardness of the alloy.

2. The final spoke tension. "Soft work" soon reaches a tolerance of zero. The work looks good, but it has no durability. Subsequent re-truing is the result. If, however, the wheel is trued using the highest permissible spoke tension, the work is more demanding, more difficult and more time consuming. The rim becomes bulky, it fights back and hardly reacts properly. Small tolerances are therefore harder to be corrected.

Whether the correction needs to be made laterally or radially, it is always the nipples at the center of the rim misalignment which should be loosened or tightened the most. The neighboring spokes are adjusted less until the end of the deformation is reached.

Rims which are not centered between the flanges, especially those on the rear wheel or on a disk braked front wheel, react differently to nipple rotations. Some rear wheels with 9-speed sprocket sets react in a ratio of 3:1. In other words, the spokes on the right hand side of the wheel influence radial deformation more than those on the left. The opposite is true for lateral deformation.

Lateral Correction

Lateral deformation is corrected by loosening and tightening the nipples in the area of the deformation. Depending on the measure of deformation, up to half a turn may be required. Final fine adjustment is made using one sixteenth of a turn.

All lateral corrections are made by loosening and tightening the nipples.

If a nipple is only loosened or only tightened, then the radial alignment will be influenced accidentally.

truing lateral

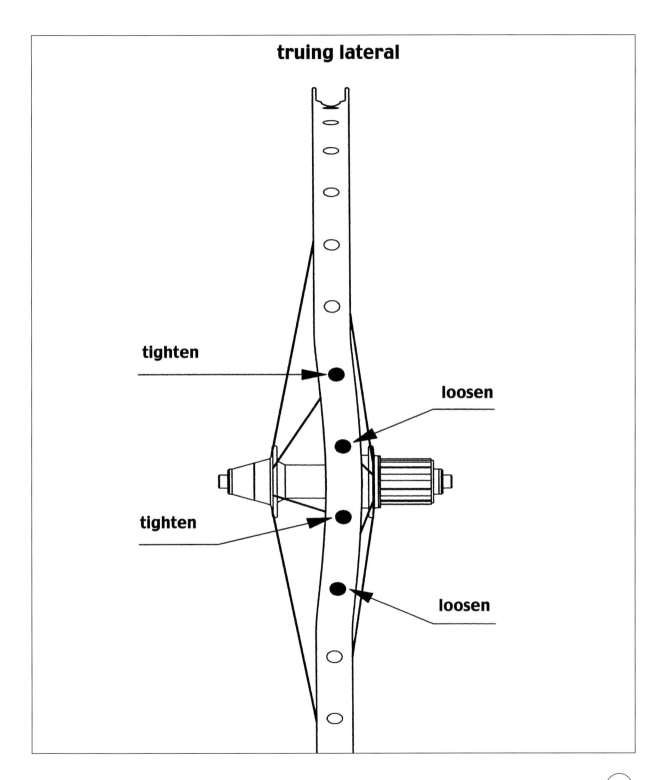

tighten

loosen

tighten

loosen

Radial Correction

If the rim is deformed inwards, nipples should be loosened. If the deformation is outwards, the nipple should be tightened. The neighboring nipples must also be adjusted in the same way. If the deformation is small, adjust the two neighboring nipples, i.e., the one to the left and the one to the right.

Dishing the rim

If the wheel geometry is such that the rim lies exactly in the center of the two hub lock nuts, then the wheel is correctly dished.

The more precise the work, the more precise the straight-line roll of the wheel and subsequently, of the bike itself. Practiced riders can take their hands off the handlebars and take refreshment

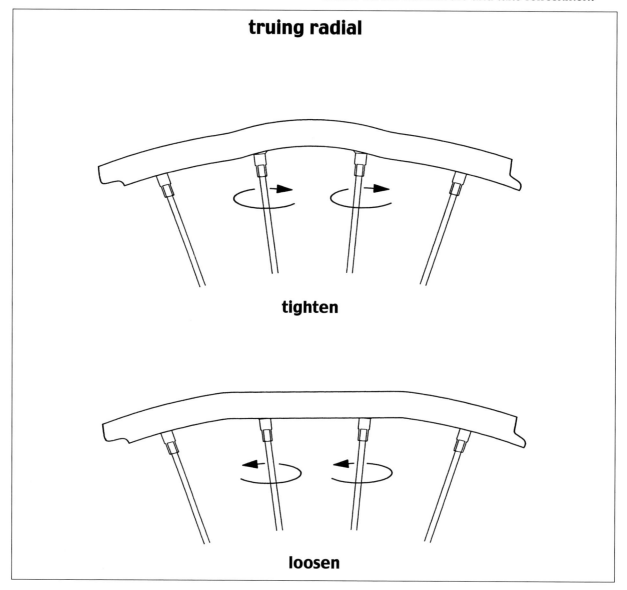

truing radial

tighten

loosen

without having to correct their riding line by body movement.

Correctly dished wheels can only function as they should when the fork ends and dropouts are precisely aligned. If they are not, this should be corrected.

Sometimes the fork ends and dropouts have been imprecisely brazed or welded in the factory. In such cases a true wheel professional would never think of simply displacing the rim as compensation for the poor workmanship on the frame. Think what could happen if such an "adjusted" wheel were later ever installed in a perfectly aligned frame.

There is an old but simple trick to check the straight-line roll of a bicycle:

- Wet both tires with generous amounts of water and push (not ride) the bike with the saddle as though you were riding hands-off over dry, flat terrain. If the tires leave a single trail, then the straight-line roll is correct.

  If, however, the tires leave two distinct trails, something is not as it should be, but seeing as we are all good wheelbuilders, then the error must be in the fork or the frame.

Dishing the rim is carried out stepwise during the centering procedure and the work checked using a dishing gauge.

The bridge-like dishing gauge is placed on the right hand side of the wheel so that it spans the rim and the adjusting screw is adjusted until it makes contact with the lock nut of the axle. It is then placed on the left hand side of the wheel without changing the position of the adjusting screw.

If there is a space

 - between the rim and the bridge, then the rim is to be pulled in the direction of the side of the wheel currently being checked.

 - between the adjusting screw and the lock nut, then the rim must be dished towards the oppo - site side than the one currently being checked.

Dishing a front wheel not equipped with disk brakes is easy, because the rim is positioned exactly in the center of the two hub flanges.

On the rear wheel, however, the rim almost extends beyond the right-hand flange. In disk-braked wheels it is somewhat closer to the left-hand flange.

During the truing stage of the rear wheel, one should try to position the rim as far to the right and as far beyond its actual central position as possible. Finish truing the wheel, install the right-hand side spokes with their optimum tension and never mind about tensioning the left-hand for the time being. The wheel is dished towards the left definitive at the end of the truing stage.

This is practically the only way to achieve the highest possible spoke tension on the left-hand side. If this is not done, then it will be very difficult to get enough tension into the left-hand spokes.

The same system can be applied to disk-braked front wheels, but in this case the rim is initially to be positioned as far in the direction of the brake disk as possible.

Checking the dished rim.

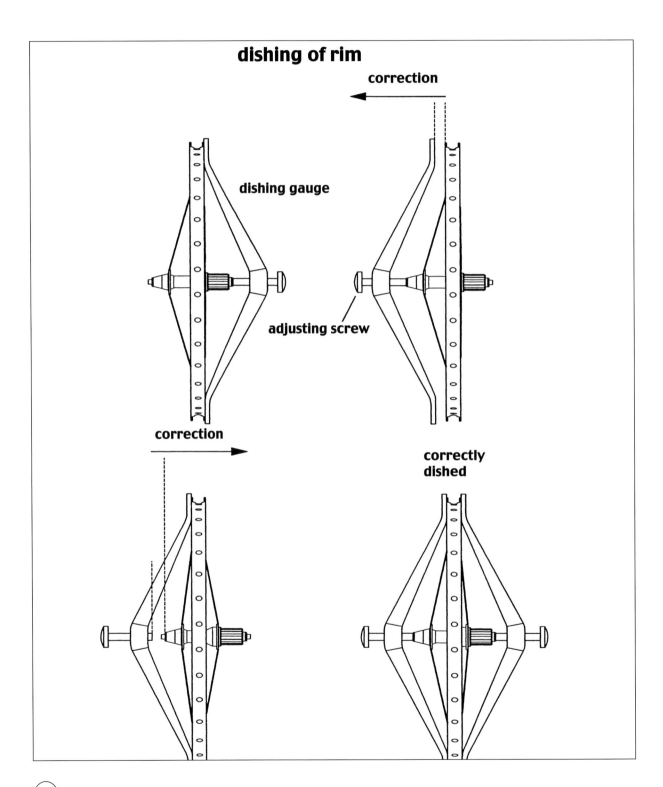

dishing of rim

correction

dishing gauge

adjusting screw

correction

correctly
dished

Spoke Alignment / Stress Relieving

When the wheel has been trued and the spokes tensioned, some spokes may not lie in a flat, straight line from the hub to the rim. Such a wheel does not yet "stand" because the spokes will adjust themselves during riding and the wheel will have to be re-trued.

This extra work can be prevented during the truing stage by holding a pair of left-hand and right-hand spokes and squeezing them together. This places the spokes under a momentary overload and straightens them where necessary.

Another small job simply involves bending the spokes at the nipple ends - the misalignment of spoke and nipple depends on the number of spokes and the spoking method used. Hold crossed pairs of spokes and squeeze them together. The spokes are made of flexible wire and so bending them in this way does no harm whatsoever.

The higher the tension of the spokes, the more they twist and will remain that way. Thicker spokes twist less than thinner spokes. Corrective measures are carried out during the truing stage, by momentarily relieving the tension of each spoke by "pressing" the wheel. A clicking noise should be clearly audible in the workshop - and not when the wheel is used for the first time.

There are a number of popular methods of stress relieving wheels, some gentler than others. Banging the spokes with your Doc Martens is *definitely* a case of overkill. The simplest method is to do the job on the workbench. Place the wheel on the bench in such a way that it rests on the axle and the 6 o'clock position of the rim. Using your left hand in the 9 o'clock and your right hand in the 3 o'clock position press the wheel in steps of approximately three spokes down towards the bench. When this side has been pressed, turn the wheel over and repeat on the other side. You should be able to hear the spokes settling. Re-true the wheel and repeat the pressing stage again until the wheel needs no more retruing. The wheel "stands" at last!

Pressing the wheel on a workbench.

The gentlest method demands a good deal of skill and "feeling." We sit down, place the wheel on our lap and hold it against our thighs with our forearms. Then we grasp the 12 o'clock position of the rim between three spokes and try to pull it upwards against the resistance of our forearms. The wheel is rotated three spokes at a time until it has completed a full rotation, then turned over and the work is repeated on the other side until all the spokes have been relieved and have adjusted themselves. Inexperienced builders should take great care when attempting the work in this manner. Cheap rims made from soft aluminum do not withstand this procedure, they will simply collapse.

The "softer" way.

Tensioning the Spokes

The standard with which a wheel "stands" is only as good as the precision of the spoke tension !

The way in which the spoke tension influences the quality of the end product, and the ideal spoke tension figures themselves has been described in detail in chapter 2, "Spoke Failure, Cause #2."

During the truing stage, the tension is increased gradually before the truing and dishing procedure. The spoke tensioning procedure should be finished before the final truing and dishing, when the wheel, having been pressed for the last time, requires no further re-truing.

The application of a tensiometer at this time is of great advantage, as, after every tensioning stage, the instrument shows us how close we are to the ideal spoke tension figure.

Checking the spoke tension.

Truing the rear wheel

Components: DT Hügi MTB hub, MAVIC X517 32-hole rim, DT Competition spokes 2.0/1.8/2.0 mm, 265 mm left, 263 mm right,

Spoking: Triple laced, symmetrical, spokes loose at first, one nipple thread turn visible.

Truing Procedure
1 Drop of oil between rim and nipple.
Tighten all right-hand nipples 5 or 6 turns, i.e. align the rim as far to the right as possible.
Tighten all left-hand nipples 2 or 3 turns.
Squeeze all spokes manually.
Pre-truing radially and laterally.
Tighten all right-hand nipples until the ideal spoke tension of 1,000 - 1,100 N (225 - 250 lbs) is reached.
Set spoke heads with punch.
Press down wheel on workbench.
Initial check for central dishing.
Tighten all left-hand nipples 1 - 1 1/2 turns.
Fine truing adjustment, radially and laterally.
Dish the rim towards the left and finalize dishing.
Squeeze all spokes by hand.
Re-check spoke tension.
Fine truing adjustment.
Press down wheel on workbench.
Re-true.
Press down wheel on workbench, re-true,repeat until the wheel "stands".
Final check: Spoke tension, trueness, dishing, wheel rotation.

Nipple locking

Correctly spoked and tensioned wheels do not usually require their nipples to be threadlocked. Yet in some cases, especially on the left-hand side of the rear wheel where the spoke tension is at its lowest, it may be necessary.

Many of my colleagues treat the spoke thread with linseed oil, WHEELSMITH'S SpokePrep or even with industrial threadlockers before installation. The first two of these products do indeed fulfill their purpose - they lubricate the thread during the truing procedure and later decrease the chance of the nipple becoming loose. Using classical industrial threadlockers only works when the thread hasn't been lubricated, but even so, the bonded area remains just that, so that a subsequent truing of the wheel is no longer possible.

At the request of many customers from all over the world, DT SWISS has worked together with the manufacturers of LOCTITE to produce a new product in liquid form called DT SPOKE FREEZE. It is applied on the finished wheel, not before the spoking stage. The characteristics of the bonding agent are such that even when used on a lubricated spoke thread, a very tenacious joint between the spoke and the nipple is attained. The wheel can therefore be retrued at any subsequent time.

DT SPOKE FREEZE is a plastic in liquid form without solvents. It has anaerobiotic setting characteristics, i.e. it sets as soon as the air is removed.

The drops of DT SPOKE FREEZE in every nipple hole are spread by capillary action between the spokes and the nipples and the bonding agent sets because air is no longer present. The wheel can be used within approximately three hours. Used wheels with problematic spokes and nipples which have already been used can also be treated with this product.

Removing and Replacing Rims

Sometimes, because of a faulty hub or the recurrence of broken spokes, it is necessary to replace all the spokes. The rim is usually undamaged and can therefore be reused.

Applying DT SPOKE FREEZE.

When removing spokes from a wheel it is important that the rim does not become permanently malformed. The rim must therefore be de-tensioned step-wise. Begin by loosening all the nipples by one wrench turn. Continue by loosening all the nipples by two wrench turns until all the spokes are hanging loose in the wheel. Finally, use a spoke cutter to cut out all the spokes close to the hub.

Wear protective gloves! Cut spokes are as sharp as needles and can cause painful injuries!

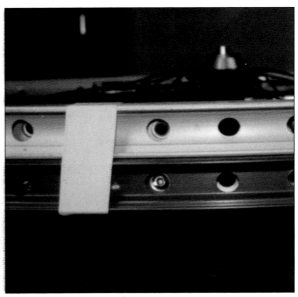
Replacing a rim.

If, however, you only wish to replace the rim, then the spoke structure with its intact spokes can be reused as long as the type of rim is the same or has the same diameter as the old one.

Clamp the wheel by the axle in a vise and loosen the nipples in two steps, as described above. Position the new rim, valve hole over valve hole on top of the old one and hold them together using adhesive tape at two to four equally spaced places.

Begin at the valve hole and unscrew the first nipple, insert the spoke into the top rim and screw a new nipple onto it (never reuse old nipples). When all spokes have been transferred to the new rim, remove the adhesive tape and finish the wheel using the truing stand.

There is no point in removing used spokes and storing them for future use. The spoke elbows and spoke heads have adapted themselves to the hub so well that they will almost certainly not fit the flanges of the new hub. Apart from that, you save so little that the work involved is just not worth it.

Tying and Soldering

Reason and Purpose

A long forgotten art, but in view of the high demands placed on today's wheels, more necessary than ever.

This especially applies to the rear wheel, the structural spoke arrangement of which is placed not only under the strain of the rider's weight but also has to cope with huge, irregular driving forces which result in an adverse shifting of the spokes when the wheels are in motion. The spoke elbows "work" in the flange, enlarge the spoke hole, become brittle under the constant stresses and subsequently fail.

On a normal rear wheel, neither tied nor soldered, it is possible to see how friction causes the surface between crossed spokes to become shiny and worn.

Tying and soldering enhances the quality of the finished wheel. The life-expectancy of the wheel

Schraner's tying and soldering tool board.

is increased enormously without influencing the tension of the spokes.

It adds stability to the spokes' crossed structure, because the hub and the spokes should form an immovable unit and - even more importantly - they should remain so. The spokes no longer move against each other and the result is a solid unity of hub and spokes.

In addition, should the wheel encounter any momentary radial stresses (bumps), the highest stress encountered by any one spoke is decreased thanks to the damping effects of its "co-soldered" neighbors. Tied and soldered spokes therefore tend to look after each other!

Yet another positive aspect is the large flange effect. A small flange hub can almost be transformed into a large flange hub. The actual flange diameter is increased to that of a large flange hub.

The wheel becomes a little harder, responds more directly when riding upright and is faster when accelerating - qualities highly appreciated by amateur and professional athletes alike.

Tying and soldering also offers advantages for the front wheel, increasing durability and allowing it to be steered more directly when riding upright.

Procedure: Brühlmann Method

As mentioned earlier, the procedure of tying and soldering fell into disuse, being practiced only on track racing wheels. Fritz Brühlmann re-invented the practice for road use and I did the same for mountainbike use.

The most important component is the correct tying wire. Fritz Brühlmann tried and tested numerous types of wire over many years and finally settled on 0,4mm thick, pre-tinned iron wire.

 -The advantages are, that when the spoke crossings have been tied, the end of the wire can simply be yanked off, making complicated knotting procedures unnecessary. Other types of wire can not be broken off as easily because they stretch too much.

 -The pre-tinned surface acts as a temperature indicator during the soldering stage. As soon as the correct temperature is reached, the tin melts and becomes shiny. Annealing and damaging the spokes is therefore prevented.

This knot-free method of tying, remembering that every tied spoke crossing should be a miniature work of art, is relatively fast, simple to learn and easy to apply. Other methods of tying are not quite as even and look less professional. Some even look quite odd and remind one of a child's first attempt at knitting.

Tools and Materials

- Brühlmann's tying wire (DT PROLINE)

- Liquid flux

- Electric soldering iron 100 Watt or propane gas soldering torch

- Soldering wire, 1mm thick (MULTICORE)

- Brass wire brush (grill cleaning brush)

General

It is important to know that it is the tying and not the soldering that gives the strength. Soldering is only carried out to prevent the wire from unwinding over a period of time.

Beginners should practice on the front wheel, as this offers more room than the rear wheel for handling the somewhat awkward spool of wire.

The spoke crossings closest to the rim are those which are to be tied and soldered.

Tying

During the entire procedure, the work is carried out using wire direct from the reel. We do not cut off small lengths in advance.

Place the end of the wire onto the spoke crossing from behind and let about 5 mm stick out towards the front. Hold both ends of the reel and wind the wire firmly around the crossing seven times. Still holding the reel firmly, take a screwdriver and push the lines of wire together so that it looks better.

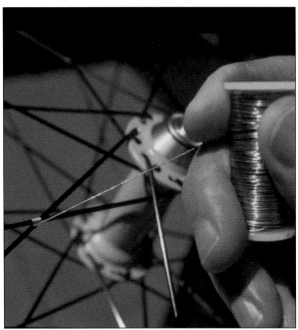
The tying job.

The spool is then taken from the inside to the outside and the wire yanked off in the direction of the hub. If the work has been done properly and the wire is nice and firm, it gives off a hard, metallic sounding note when plucked.

See the drawing on the following page.

Soldering

Beginners are better off using an electric soldering iron, as this makes it impossible to overheat the spokes.

The spoke crossing is heated only for as long as it takes for the tin surface of the tying wire to begin to melt - it becomes visibly shiny.

Remove the heat, apply the soldering wire and reheat.

Excessive soldering material in its liquid state is knocked off using a 14/15mm box end wrench (ideal weight, round edges), to make the wound wire well visible and the job looks well done. Work done by professionals is immediately recognizable, whereas amateurs tend to produce a lot

of excess weight.

When the solder is cool, place the wheel over a bucket filled with hot water and detergent and use the wire brush to clean all the tied crossings.

Hang the wheel up to dry. The following day, add a drop of oil (to prevent rust) to every tie and clean with a dry cloth. A manual "squeeze test" of the spokes will show that the spoke structure will remain stable even when placed under extreme stresses.

The soldering work.

Self-criticism is a must during the tying procedure. I still have to untie and improve my work sometimes, when I'm not quite up to my usual form.

tying direct from wire spool

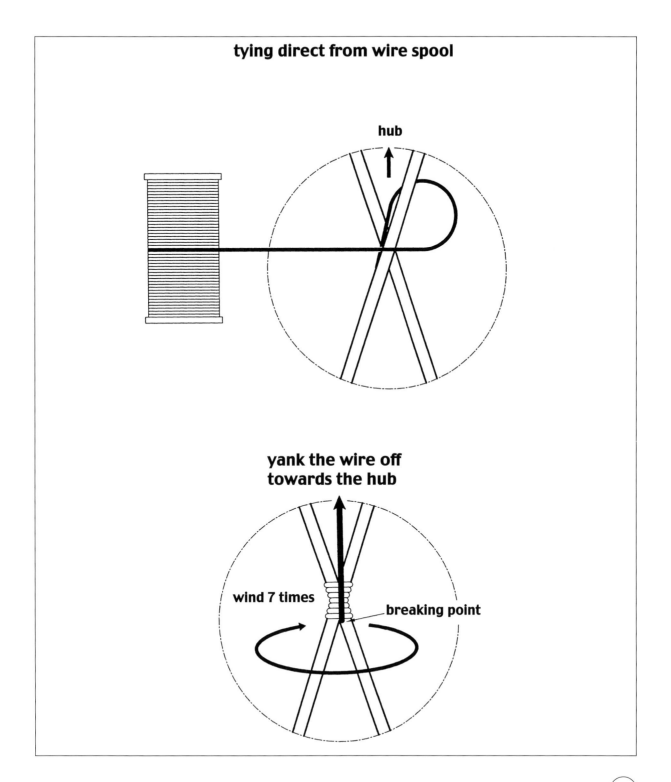

hub

yank the wire off
towards the hub

wind 7 times

breaking point

Corking Rims

An old trick, but one which is becoming increasingly popular again, is corking the rim eyelets.

With this method, the gluing surface area for tubular tires is increased and, in addition, the eyelets don't become filled with rim cement.

Narrow clincher tires on racing bikes require high pressure but the rim tape can not always cope with it. They form tears over the eyelets and result in sudden inner tube failure. This is a typical case for corking the eyelets.

You can buy the cork from a bike shop or even from a drug store. Like a cork in a bottle, they should have a firm seat without having to be glued into place. Overlapping areas are cut off or rubbed down using sandpaper.

Folding-type clinchers are at greatest risk of an inner tube failure. If the rider is unable to brake immediately, the tire often slips off the rim and can become entangled in the front fork or in the area around the rear fork resulting in disastrous accidents. Such occurrences can be avoided by gluing an additional cotton (VELOX) rim tape onto the first, synthetic (MICHELIN) rim tape. The circumference of the rim bed is thus increased and it is more difficult for the flat tire to jump off the rim. This practice, however, requires at least two tire levers and more strength to remove the tire.

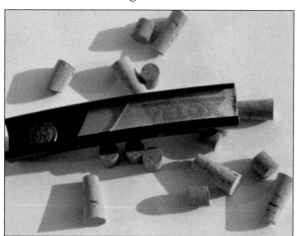
Corking rims.

Slotting Hubs (Aero-Spokes)

Aero-spokes can not simply be fitted into the normal, circular drilled holes in the flange, because the flattened midsection of the spoke is too wide.

Instead of simply drilling out the spoke holes, the professional wheelbuilder prefers a better method, developed by Fritz Brühlmann. Using a handsaw bow fitted with a 1.6 mm diameter round profiled saw blade on each spoke hole, file a slot towards the hub axle.

The job is easier if you clamp the area of the hub between the lock-nuts in a vise, rather like you do with the frame and forks, so that the wheel itself can still be rotated. Mark a starting point with a felt-tipped pen. Open the saw, insert the blade into the spoke hole, close the saw and file the slot towards the axle.

Wheels equipped with aero-spokes are often radially spoked, but this places the flange under immense tensile loads. For this reason, both on the front and rear wheels, absolute precision is a must and the slots should only be as small and as narrow as they need be.

Not knowing any better, some wheelbuilders used to file the slot at a tangent to the flange, or cut them out using special pliers which resulted in so-called "button holes". The spacing between the slots was, however, too narrow and the high occurrences of "exploded" wheel flanges put an end to this practice.

Small flange hubs with over 28 spoke holes - or 32 holes if they are made by a reliable manufacturer - are not suitable for such a modification because of the small amount of flange material between the individual spoke holes.

Slotting hubs requires not only a good deal of dexterity but also a good feeling for the material you are working with.

According to the rules of product liability, if flanges equipped with aero-spokes break, the responsibility lies neither with the manufacturers of the hub and spokes, nor with the author of this book, but only with the person who carried out the modification!

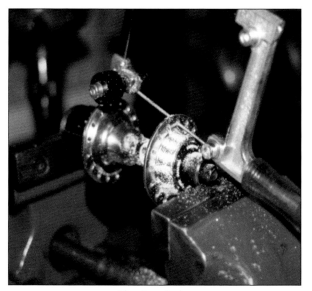

Slotting hubs.

Checking.

Amateurs should therefore refrain from carrying out this work themselves. Appropriate hubs for use with aero-spokes are already available (SHIMANO, DT HÜGI). The modification to these hubs is not carried out manually, but by CNC machines before the hubs are anodized.

Wheel Repairing

Removing the tire for each wheel repair is recommended. This simplifies the work of replacing nip-ples and also makes it easier to check whether a spoke is sticking up, or whether the rim tape is still undamaged. Radial misalignments of the rim can also only be corrected when the tire is removed.

For simple retruing jobs, where no spokes need replacing, one follows the same procedure as that used for a new wheel.

Should any spokes require replacement, it is imperative that you also replace the nipples.

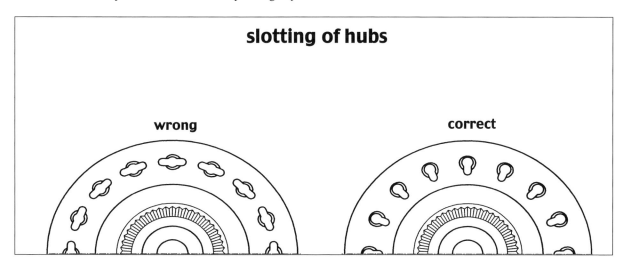

slotting of hubs

wrong   correct

When replacing spokes which have broken at the elbow always use a washer under the new spoke.

After the repair has been carried out, check the tension of every spoke on the wheel and - in most cases - increase the tension. If spokes later still tend to break on the wheel then I recommend replacing every spoke, using a washer beneath each one.

Accidents cause the rim to misalign or, in severe cases, bend. If a retruing of the wheel fails to restore its original circularity, the rim should be replaced. Despite the high price of some rims they should nevertheless be seen as a throw-away commodity. They are sorely misused by riding and braking and with time they lose much of their elasticity and become sluggish.

So my advice is, forget rim repairs. The days in which dents were carefully hammered out are long past - it simply is not worth the effort or the time. It is especially inexplicable to find such efforts still being applied to expensive bikes.

Wheelbuilding time and costs

Wheelbuilding requires a good deal of time and your full concentration!

The work involves numerous steps, among them:

- determining the correct spoke length
- preparing the rim, hub and spokes (possibly with washers)
- laterally and radially truing the wheel
- dishing the rim
- perfecting the spoke tension and
- repeatedly stress relieving the wheel

Use your full concentration - this is no time for daydreaming, neither is the work. Avoid being disturbed and make sure you are in the right mood. Only then will wheelbulding be a pleasurable task.

Ferdy Kübler, winner of the 1950 Tour de France and World Road Champion in 1951, visits the author in his workshop, 1992.

The craftsmanship

It is impossible to build high quality wheels all day long. Concentration tends to drift after a few hours, you get into a routine and the fine quality of the wheel suffers.

I see myself as an experienced wheelbuilder and I personally spend at least one hour on one wheel, be it a rear or a front wheel.

If I took less time the spoke tension would be insufficient, or the wheel, although being perfectly circular, would not last very long. Because the wheel doesn't "stand." The result is that the wheel in use will have to be retrued, while spoke failure is just a question of time.

He or she who is not prepared to spend the kind of time or money described in these pages should leave the work to others and instead purchase good quality wheels from a respectable source.

Tying and soldering, a fiddly job requiring a certain amount of practice, calls for an additional 30 minutes. A similar amount of time is necessary for slotting hubs for the use of aero spokes.

DANIEL GISIGER

Daniel Gisiger - Fast wheels

In 1983, when aero-spokes were still a novelty, I was a rookie mechanic at 6-day races and I decided to build myself a pair of track wheels using 36 DT New Aero spokes on each, fitting them radially on the front wheel and quad-crossed on the back wheel. The idea was to put these wheels at the disposal of top racers for decisive Madison races.

Daniel Gisiger, a well-known track and road racer, on his very best form in 1983 (winning both the Grand Prix des Nations and the Baracchi Trophy), hired me as the mechanic for the Grenoble Six-Day race, an event he was simply itching to win. Before the decisive final I fit my fast wheels without even asking him. He was skeptical about my voluntary modification and was unsure about them when he went out onto the track. The race turned into a hair-raising duel between two teams hungry for the win (Vallet/Michaud and Gisiger/Clerc. Neither team managed to win the all-important lap, but then Vallet/Michaud missed a changeover just before the end of the race.

Both rider and mechanic are not-so-fresh looking at the end of a hard Six-Day night, Zürich, 1988.

From then on, these wheels played their part in further successes for Gisiger. They formed the basis of a solid, trusting relationship between rider and mechanic. We became friends for life.

Good wheels and good legs! Gisiger at the Six-Days of Zürich, 1983.

After the Zürich Six-Day race in 1983, I was asked to sell him the wheels. I was to look after them carefully, lock them away when they were not in use - and they were used sparingly - only for Gisiger's important, decisive races. For this reason, I always knew what he was planning and what his physical condition was. At his last track race, an Omnium, in 1989 in Copenhagen, Gisiger was accidently hit by another rider and the wheels were damaged beyond repair.

The wheels died on the same day that a great career of a great rider ended!

The craftsmanship

Albert Zweifel

ber of road races and tours, once in the Tour de France, once in the Giro d'Italia and 16 times in the Tour de Suisse. He improved the excellent condition he gained in this way by another novelty at the time - being paced by a motorcycle in order to improve the consistency of his speed and his experience of high pedaling rates.

He also set new standards for the selection of materials. For every race he used five sets of cross country bikes, identical down to the smallest detail and all equally highly-polished. His helpers were all dressed in the same uniform and thus were clearly identifiable around the circuit. Each of them had a small box of tools, greasing and cleaning materials with them. His wheels, all of which were built by me, were made from MAVIC SSC rims with 32 hard-tensioned DT Competition 2.0/1.8/2.0 mm spokes and brass nipples.

His love for detail and for perfection brought him success. He was World Champion in 1976, 1977, 1978, 1979 and once again in 1986.

Albert Zweifel - The perfectionist

In the '70s, training for the sport of cross-country racing was still rudimentary. Every rider had his own methods and it wasn't taken that seriously.

Albert was the first rider of international standing who worked with a paid fitness coach. To prepare for the winter he used to take part in a large num-

SILVIA FURST

Silvia Fürst - Instinct for the possible

In my view, Silvia, the Mountain-bike Cross Country World Champion 1992 and at the head of her field for years, is a remarkable exception to the rule.

She appears shy and modest, yet when she is in her biking element she has a finely tuned instinct for exactly how much her bike can take. Unlike many of her male and female colleagues of the mountain-bike world, who trash every machine they sit on, Silvia has that certain feeling for the way that good material needs to be treated. Before every season she gets two sets of specially-built wheels from me, with MAVIC 217/517 rims, 32 DT Revolution 2.0/1.5/2.0 mm spokes, tied and soldered, with aluminum nipples.

Silvia Fürst

She uses these for an entire year, in World Cup races, national and international Championships and gives them back to me at the end of the season. Apart from signs of brake scarring around the rims, there has never been any damage to them - they look almost like new, are still fully circular and still "stand."

PART 4

Around the wheel

New products
Further training

Around the wheel

New Products

The future of any branch of industry is dependent on its capability of constantly developing innovative techniques and products.

The bicycle industry is no exception. It needs new ideas and new products - and not necessarily originating from household names - to continue to attract new generations of bike enthusiasts. Numerous independent inventors, some of which are new to the bicycling world, crop up every year and display astounding enthusiasm and dedication. Take them seriously and mentally salute them. Sometimes their innovations are simply yesterday's warmed-up leftovers, some are just too weird or too advanced for the current market. Some inventors are too impatient and begin to realize their next idea before the last is mature enough for production, while ignoring an important factor - marketing.

But time has shown that innovations from such sources constantly lead to progress in the two-wheel industry. For this reason one should never be too quick to sneer. Be skeptical, by all means, but think it over, try it and then make your judgement.

Some big-name component manufacturers tend to wallow in overkill when it comes to new products.

Tough, even brutal marketing strategies are the order of the day. At the same time they cause uneasiness and worry among users and the trade. Perhaps they should consider gentle persuasion instead of attacking from all angles?

Looking back, it seems as though technical development of road bikes had reached the point of stagnation shortly before the appearance of the mountain-bike. As this branch evolved, both areas profited from each other.

Offroad machines adopted the clipless pedals which road cyclists had used for years, while handlebar gear shifters, a common sight on mountain-bikes, were being installed on road bikes. Down-tube shifters are a rare sight these days.

Wheels have also been able to profit from innovation. For example

- Spokes
  - with much narrower midsections,
  - made of titanium and with
  - colored abrasive resistant surfaces.

- Nipples
  - made from aluminum, stronger;
  - anodized, colored or neutral.
- Hubs
  - with industrial bearings
  - power transmission with star ratchets instead of pawls (DT-Hügi).
- Rims
  - rim joints welded and machined instead of butted (MAVIC)
  - ceramic-coated brake surfaces
  - anodized surfaces, colored or neutral
  - CAD-designed, lighter yet more stable rim cross sections.

Centurion Renner. Wheelbuilding Seminar, Magstatt, Germany, February, 1998.

Further Training

I have attempted to write down all my knowledge and all my secrets and tricks of the trade in this book. What I cannot put into words is the practical use of tools and wheel components.

Wheelbuilding is a specialized field in which one can never learn too much. You have to keep up with the constant development and progress made in bike technology. You have to adapt. You learn something new every day, by your own experience, during discussions with clients, and especially during discussions with colleagues at bike shows and at wheelbuilding seminars.

Over 700 participants of the first series of DT SWISS's Wheelbuilding Seminars in the USA

received a diploma as a DT Certified Wheel-builder. My friends Tim Breen and Richard Wade, both wheelbuilding teaching authorities attended the seminars as instructors. I was able to learn a lot from them, as well as from Alan Schiff, the latest member of the DT SWISS Instructors Team. We're all wheelaholics and we all, as we say in Switzerland "have our hay in the same loft," meaning that we all use the same working and instruction methods.

Chatting with wheelbuilding pros at the Interbike tradeshow in Anaheim, 1997.

Illustration and Photo Credits

All drawings are under trademark and copyright of
DT SWISS AG.

Page 11, © Reinhard.

Page 12, upper left, © Schraner; lower left
© HOLLAND MECHANICS.

Page 13, © HOLLAND MECHANICS.

Page 14, © Presse 'E Sports.

Page 18, © DT SWISS.

Page 23, all © Schraner.

Page 24, top left © Schraner, top right and bottom left,
© DT SWISS.

Page 26, © DT SWISS.

Page 29, © DT SWISS.

Page 30, © DT SWISS.

Page 31, all © DT SWISS.

Page 32, © DT SWISS.

Page 34, unknown.

Page 36, lower left, © Joller, upper right unknown.

Page 37, unknown.

Page 38, lower left and top right,
© Fischer Media; lower right © Schraner.

Page 40, unknown.

Page 41, © DT SWISS.

Page 42, all © Schraner.

Page 47, © Schraner.

Page 56, © Schraner.

Page 60, © Joller.

Page 64, all © Schraner.

Page 65, © Schraner.

Page 66, © Joller.

Page 75, © Joller.

Page 76, © Schraner.

Page 77, upper and lower left © Schraner, upper right,
© PARK TOOLS.

Page 78, all © Joller.

Page 79, © Joller.

Page 80, © Kovacs.

Page 83, © Kovacs.

Page 85, all © Joller.

Page 86, © Kovacs.

Page 87, upper right © Joller; lower right © Schraner.

Page 88, © Schraner.

Page 90, all © Joller.

Page 92, © Schraner.

Page 93, all © Schraner

Page 94, unknown.

Page 96, unknown.

Page 97, unknown.

Page 98, © Martin Platter.

Page 101, © Schraner.

Page 102, © Schraner.

Glossary of Terms

alloy - A mixture of a pure metal and lesser amounts of other metals; used to form a material with different properties.

buckling - Side deflection of a column or cylinder in compression.

butted spoke - see swaged or forged spoke.

bracing angle - angle the spoke makes in relation to the plane of a wheel or rim.

cassette hub - rear hub with integral freewheel and bearing.

cog set - sprockets mounted on a freewheel.

compression - pushing force.

clincher - a tire with a casing whose bead is designed to set in a rim with grooved sidewalls.

deflection - change in shape resulting from an applied force.

deformation - temporary or permanent deflections.

derailleur - mechanism that shifts a bicycle chain from one sprocket to another.

dished wheel - wheel whose rim is not centered between its hub flanges; rear wheel; asymmetric wheel.

drive side - cassette body side of a bicycle wheel.

ductile - plastic deformation without failure.

dynamic - changing, variable, moving.

elastic - deforms with total recovery.

elastic limit - boundary between plastic and elastic deformation.

flange - circular portion of a bicycle hub for attaching spokes.

flange diameter - diameter of the center of the spoke hole in the flange.

freehub - cassette hub; integral hub and freewheel.

freewheel - a mechanism with multiple sprockets that rotates in a single direction.

galling - surface welding between two metals by unlubricated sliding.

gauge (spoke) - English measure of wire diameters; 14 gauge = 2.0 mm, 15 gauge = 1.8 mm, 16 gauge = 1.6 mm, 17 gauge = 1.5 mm.

hub - central unit of a wheel that rotates on its axle and on whose flange the spokes are laced.

hub body - portion of hub that connects its flanges.

hub diameter - flange diameter.

inbound spoke - spoke that projects into the hub on insertion.

interlacing - placing outbound spokes under tube.

hub shaft - portion of hub that connects its flanges.

inbound spoke - spoke that projects into the hub on insertion.

interlacing - placing outbound spokes under inbound spokes at their outer crossing.

kilogram - Unit of mass; 1 kg = 2.2 pounds.

lateral - from side-to-side.

metal - structural material; iron, steel, aluminum, brass, titanium, etc.

meter (m) - SI unit of length; m = 39.37 inches.

millimeter (mm) - unit of length; 1/1000 m = 1/25.4 inch.

mode (vibration) - in the first mode the whole spoke swings like a jump rope, in the second mode one half is up while the other is down.

Newton (N) - unit of force exerted by one kg mass acted on by gravity (g = 9.8 m/sec 2), N=kg/g.

outbound spoke - spoke that projects out of the hub on insertion.

presta valve - common on high performance bicycle tires; with locking stem instead of a return spring.

pulling spoke - spoke that is lengthened when the wheel is in motion.

pushing spoke - spoke that is shortened when the wheel is in motion.

radial - a line originating from a central point in common.

rim - outer portion of a wheel on which the tire is mounted and to which spokes are fixed.

rim compression - force on a rim derived from spoke tension and tire air pressure.

sew-up tire - tire casing that is sewn to enclose its tube; tubular tire.

SI - Systeme Internationale (metric units).

spoke - wire that connects hub to rim.

spoke nipple - tubular threaded nut used to tension spokes.

sprocket - toothed wheel to engage a chain.

static - fixed, unchanging, constant.

stiffness - force per unit deformation (N/m).

Notes

Notes

Notes

Notes

Notes